?d,

Tickenham

Avon.

BS21 6RF

STEEP HOLM
— a case history in the
study of evolution

STEEP HOLM
— a case history in the study of evolution

Kenneth Allsop Trust
and John Fowles

Kenneth Allsop Memorial Trust

Distributed by Dorset Publishing Co
Knock-na-cre, Milborne Port,
Sherborne, Dorset DT9 5HJ

Dedicated to the Watts family, boatmen of
Weston-super-Mare — and in particular Frank,
John, Ian and Mike — who, with their helpers,
operate the island's ferry service. Without them,
progress would have remained a dream.

First published 1978 in Great Britain by Kenneth Allsop
Memorial Trust Limited, Knock-na-cre, Milborne Port,
Sherborne, Dorset DT9 5HJ. Chapters copyright the respective
writers © Rodney Legg, John Fowles, Betty Allsop, Cuillin
Bantock, Colin Graham and Tony Parsons 1978. Photographs
© Colin Graham, 1978. No part of this publication may be
reproduced, stored in a retrieval system, or transmitted in any
form or by any means, electronic, mechanical, photocopying,
recording or otherwise, without prior permission of the Kenneth
Allsop Memorial Trust. Trade orders should be sent to Dorset
Publishing Company, Milborne Port, Sherborne, Dorset DT9 5HJ.
ISBN 0 902129 29 5.

Production by Dorset Publishing Company, Milborne Port,
Sherborne, Dorset, with darkroom work on all plates by
Malcolm Noyes.
Island map drawn by Malcolm Noyes.
Peregrine emblem sketched by Richard Fowling on the spot
during an island sighting.
Typesetting by Jennie Duley at Maddison Publicity, East Street,
Milborne Port, Sherborne, Dorset.
Layouts by Jonathan S. Hebert of Photo-graphics at Lower Lye
Farmhouse, Yarcombe, Honiton, Devon.
Printing by Redwood Burn Limited at Yeoman Way, Trowbridge,
Wiltshire.
Cased in buckram by the Binding Division of Redwood Burn
Limited at Royal Mills, Esher, Surrey.
Promotion by Pauline Yesson at the mainland office of the
Kenneth Allsop Memorial Trust, Knock-na-cre, Milborne Port,
Sherborne, Dorset DT9 5HJ, telephone 0963 32583.
For details about visiting the island, together with a booking
form and information on Trust membership, send a medium
sized stamped-and-addressed envelope to Kenneth Allsop Island,
Knock-na-cre, Milborne Port, Sherborne, Dorset DT9 5HJ.

Contents

The impetus for this book was to present a case for the conservation of an island wild life sanctuary, in memory of naturalist Kenneth Allsop. The result is a record of all that is known about Steep Holm, a rocky fifty acres in the middle of the Bristol Channel.

Landsnails and evolution

Cuillin Bantock

NOWADAYS MOST people believe that evolution occurs. Although it is a truism to observe that each animal and plant species is adapted for a particular life style, the consequences of having to live under different and varying environmental conditions are less immediately obvious. Some of these conditions may make opposing demands on the organism. It follows that successful adaptation of the organism, and of the population of which the organism is a part, must inevitably be a compromise evolutionary solution. A balance must be maintained between what is desirable and what is possible.

It is well known that Darwin was the first to suggest that natural selection played a part in the way in which evolution might occur. His theory of evolution by natural selection, published in an extended form as the *Origin of Species* has had a profound effect on the development of biology in the last 120 years. Variation between the individuals making up a population is so fundamental that we take it for granted.

Darwin seems to have been the first to consider its significance. His expression 'survival of the fittest' implies that differences in fitness are conferred by variation and that selection will favour the more fit. The student of evolution is especially concerned with how variation arises, with estimating how much variation exists in natural populations, with determining how important it may be as an evolutionary strategy, and with the ways in which natural selection may operate on it. On one hand he is concerned with how a balance in the response to different environmental pressures is achieved and on the other with the long term changes which can result in the formation of a new species.

Many students of biology consider evolution to be the massive changes which convert, for example, fishes into tetrapods. They are correct, but it is necessary to point out that such changes are made up in innumerable small adaptive responses in which the genetic material is gradually moulded by natural selection. These small micro-evolutionary changes occur, of course, without the conscious participation of the species concerned, although the language used to describe them is frequently teleological.

Island populations have always been of interest to the evolutionary biologist. Environmental conditions are frequently very different from those elsewhere, so that a comparison between the populations of a species living under them with those living on the mainland may reveal which components of variation are the most important to a species when it adapts to new circumstances.

The landsnail *Cepaea nemoralis* on Steep Holm, a fifty acre island in the Bristol Channel, illustrates rather well some of the principles of evolutionary biology. Its study also illustrates the difficulty of making complete statements about any biological system since the system itself is the product of multiple environmental pressures, many of which are imponderable. The work that has so far been carried out suggests that the snail has responded in several ways simultaneously to conditions on Steep Holm. One of these responses has involved a change of such magnitude that the island population may well prove to be effectively another species.

Cepaea nemoralis lends itself particularly well to the study of evolution. As is well known the shell is very variable in appearance, the most obvious component of the variation being shell colour and banding; less obvious is variation in shell size. The colour and banding variation is discontinuous, or polymorphic, since each type is clearly distinguishable from any other and there are no intermediates.

The ground colour of the shell can be brown, pink, or yellow and the horizontal bands, usually dark brown in colour, can vary in number from zero (unbanded) to five (five-banded). In contrast, variation in adult shell size is metric, or continuous. There are considerable differences in shell size (usually recorded as maximum diameter) between colonies, but the amount of variation in any one colony is small.

These two variables have been the subject of comparative studies, both between different parts of Steep Holm itself, and between Steep Holm and the mainland:-

1: *Variation between colonies on Steep Holm — shell colour* For a variable character to be of any long term evolutionary use to a species, it is necessary that it bears at least some degree of heritability. The colour and banding polymorphism of *Cepaea* is totally genetic; it is unaffected by diet or by the vegetation in which the animals live. Clearly, if the snails could "change colour", the polymorphism would not be a very reliable indicator of long term evolutionary adjustment.

Notwithstanding the conspicuousness of the polymorphism the reasons for its existence are unclear. Many gastropods possess a colour and banding polymorphism but probably in no other species is it so well developed. However, an idea of its importance is given by the following general features of *Cepaea* colonies.

The first is that there are usually considerable differences in the relative frequencies of the different types (or morphs) between colonies, even those which are close enough together to have some migration between them. Such differences are stable through successive generations. Differences in morph (or gene) frequency could result from totally random processes, but as the differences are maintained in spite of migration it strongly suggests that directional selection is taking place. This is a type of selection which favours one type at the expense of others in a colony so that it occurs at a high frequency. Intercolony differences could be produced by selection which differed in direction in different places. That directional selection is at least in part responsible is suggested by the fact that the differences often occur in relation to obvious features of the environment.

This type of selection, which produces micro-evolutionary change, will tend to reduce the amount of variation in a population; in *Cepaea* it could be expected to produce monomorphism. For example if yellow shell colour is favoured in a particular place why does not selection eliminate all the other colours?

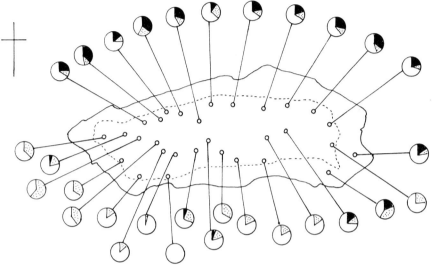

Figure 1   Map of Steep Holm to show the relative frequencies of the shell colour morphs of Cepaea nemoralis in 30 colonies. The dotted line represents the upper limit of the sea cliffs. The approximate position of each colony is indicated by a small circle. Morph frequencies are indicated by pie-diagrams in which an angle of 45° represents a frequency of 25%.

Solid: % brown
Stippled: % pink
White: % yellow

The second feature of *Cepaea* colonies is the almost universal occurrence of the polymorphism throughout the species' range, in spite of very pronounced inter-colony differences in morph frequency. This suggests that there must be a balancing selective force which opposes directional change, and which therefore maintains polymorphic variation in the snail populations.

C. nemoralis on Steep Holm nicely illustrates the above points. All the colonies are polymorphic for colour and banding. Two shell colours occur in most colonies and at least two banding types. However there are very strong differences between the colonies in relation to their aspect from which it is possible to infer the action of directional selection. *C. nemoralis* is widely distributed on the island, especially where there is ground-covering vegetation, and where the vegetation is mixed in type. It is particularly common in the rather open plant communities at the south-west end of the island and in the nettle-and-bramble communities on the north slopes of the plateau which dominate the island.

It occurs everywhere in the alexanders meadow where there is sufficient ground-cover, usually of ground ivy. Figure 1 shows the distribution of the three colour morphs in thirty colonies sampled at various points on the island in 1972. Only one of these contains only a single colour morph (yellow), from the south side of the island at Split Rock. It is immediately obvious from the figure that the distribution of the colour types is non-random. The brown morph is far more abundant on the north facing slope of the island; the average frequency on this side of the island is twenty-three per cent compared with only three per cent on the south facing slope. The difference in the frequency of the brown morph between the two slopes is statistically highly significant; the probability of the pattern being due to chance is less than one per cent. While random processes could be responsible for the inter-colony differences, they are unlikely to have caused the difference between the two sides of the island.

The association between colour morph frequency and aspect (rather than with the vegetation as such) suggests that a climatic factor is responsible. Temperature differences are the most likely. Insolation will obviously be greater on a south facing slope, and there is circumstantial evidence that this is an important factor affecting other biological systems on Steep Holm. The unusual plant communities on the island have a strong overall southern and oceanic element. Species with a geographically southern distribution such as the mallow, golden samphire, and rock sea lavender are found on Steep Holm, and especially on the south and west-facing slopes. The extremely rare wild leek occurs only on the southern slopes of Steep Holm and in the Channel Islands.

That the temperature regime between the two sides of the island is different is further indicated by the distribution of the small helicid snails *Helicella virgata* and *H. caperata.* On the mainland these snails are common in sunny sites on well drained calcareous soils; on Steep Holm they are found only on the southern and western slopes and do not seem to occur at all on the north side of the island. Finally, colour morph frequency variation in *C. nemoralis* on a major geographical scale provides indirect evidence that temperature is important. J.S. Jones has shown that the yellow morph is common towards the southern limit of the species' range.

To infer from distributional data that temperature affects morph frequency is by no means to prove that it does so. In spite of the apparent suitability of *Cepaea* for experimentation, and the large body of field data suggesting it, surprisingly little work has been carried out attempting to demonstrate climatic selection. One of the reasons for this is that results from experiments on snails in incubators may not be particularly helpful in trying to interpret patterns of gene frequency variation in the wild, and conversely the problems of trying to demonstrate selection by climate in the field are dauntingly complex.

For these reasons the present author has spent considerable time devising experimental procedures which "meet the snail halfway"—in the field, but under conditions where behaviour and mortality can be assessed relatively easily. These procedures involve the use of wire enclosures, or of population cages. The cages can be set up in a variety of sites and planted with vegetation suitable for snails.

They are completely enclosed with wire mesh which prevents egress of the snails, excludes predators, but which allows the snails to be exposed to the weather. The following accounts refers to an experiment carried out using snails from Steep Holm.

Plate 1,a. shows the situation of the Leonard Wills Field Centre at Nettlecombe in West Somerset, where the author has carried out numerous field experiments. The Centre is on a valley floor which is sheltered by steep hills on three sides. A meteorological station (visible in the plate) near the Centre shows that the valley bottom experiences an unusually continental temperature regime; the daily range sometimes exceeds 20°C. This is due mainly to low night minima but also to higher than average daily maxima, and is in obvious contrast to the maritime climate of Steep Holm.

During the winter of 1971 a wire enclosure, covering 60sq.m. was built near the meteorological station at Nettlecombe, Plate 1,a & b. The ground within was planted with nettles, dock and grass; by the following August the vegetation was well established and seemed very suitable for snails. During this month 541 live adult *C. nemoralis* were removed from various colonies on Steep Holm—mainly from those on the north slope; each shell was unique-marked with small drill holes near the lip so that the fate of the snails could be determined. The snails were put in the enclosure on 14 August 1972. The population was sampled twice yearly (usually in April and September) until the April of 1975 when it was decided to modify the experiment. On each sampling occasion just under half the total known to be present was found.

This part of the experiment failed to demonstrate natural selection; on the contrary it showed that snails from a locality as different from Nettlecombe as Steep Holm were perfectly capable of surviving when introduced into suitable vegetation subjected to a very different gross climate! Only nineteen of the snails were found dead between April 1973 and April 1975, and the recapture data show no sign of any one morph surviving better at any time than any other. The suitability of the vegetation for snails is indicated by its rapid and extensive colonisation by *C. hortensis,* which, being smaller, was able to gain access through the chicken wire from local colonies.

In contrast to the results from the wire enclosure, experiments carried out during 1973 and 1974 with population cages, using snails from various localities, showed that conditions in the cages were sufficiently stressful to induce considerable mortality over the course of several months. On 25 May 1975, 224 of the original snails were transferred to the single population cage (80cmx64cmx64cm), arrowed in Plate I,b. planted with nettles and dock. The cage was sampled for mortality on 25 July; live snails were returned and the cage resampled on 22 August when the experiment was concluded. The data are given in Table 1.

Several trends are apparent. During the first two months of this part of the experiment twenty-nine per cent of the snails died, compared with only 3.5% during the previous two and a half years. During the last part (August) seventy-seven per cent of the remaining snails died. This shows clearly that as one might expect conditions in the cage were far more stringent than in the enclosure, even though the vegetation was approximately similar. The initial source of stress in the cages is probably overcrowding. The unlikely alternative explanation is that these snails "were going to die anyway" and would have done so irrespective of their being put in a cage.

Table 1

Morph	Live snails Put out 25/5/75	dead 25/7/75	% dead	dead 22/8/75	% dead
BO	19	6	32	9	69
B3/345	18	5	28	10	77
B5	17	5	29	9	75
PO	6	2	33	3	75
P3/345	15	5	33	7	70
P5	38	17	44	16	76
YO	24	6	25	13	72
Y3/345	33	9	27	20	83
Y5	54	11	20	35	81
	224	66	29	122	77

Abbreviations: B= brown, P= pink, Y= yellow shell colour.
3/345 = shells with only the third band or with only bands 3, 4 and 5.
0 = unbanded
5 = five-banded

More interesting than the sharp increase in mortality is that the deaths appear to have been selective with respect to colour. During the period 25.5.75–25.7.75 only twenty-four per cent of the yellow-shelled snails died compared with thirty-seven per cent of the pink and thirty per cent of the brown. The difference in survival between pink and brown-shelled snails is not significant so that they can be combined and considered as a single group of 'non-yellow' shells.

The difference in survival between yellows and non-yellows is significant; $X^2(1)$ =3.86, which has a probability of occurring by chance of less than five per cent. The direction of the selection is suggestive. June and July were particularly hot at Nettlecombe in 1975. The combination of stress induced by overcrowding with higher-than-average daily temperatures may have resulted in conditions which allowed yellow-shelled snails to survive better than the others. The result is consis-

Opposite: The Nettlecombe valley in West Somerset, in which experiments on snails from Steep Holm have been carried out.
A. General view of the snail garden from the south west. The building on the left is the Leonard Wills Field Centre. The area defined by lines is the wire enclosure in which snails were kept from 1972—75. The arrow indicates the meteorological station.
B. A close-up view of the wire enclosure. In the foreground is a row of population cages. The one arrowed was used to house Steep Holm snails.

tent with the interpretation given to the field data and is also consistent with the results of an incubator experiment carried out in France by M. Lamotte in which yellow (unbanded) snails survived better than pink five-banded ones at high temperatures. The results described here appear to be the first to demonstrate selection favouring yellows in a field experiment.

In other population cage experiments carried out at Nettlecombe it has sometimes been found that there are differences in survival between snails collected from different places. It is thus possible that the results of the experiment using Steep Holm snails do not reflect differences in survival between morphs, but rather differences in survival between snails from different parts of the island. Since the snails were collected from a number of different colonies with different morph frequencies, it is arguable that populations with higher frequencies of yellow are more resistant than yellow-shelled individuals as such, irrespective of population.

However, differences in survival between snails from different populations tend to be reduced by keeping the snails under similar conditions before putting them out in cages. It follows that the original differences do not have a wholly genetic basis and are partly the result of acquired acclimatization to particular conditions. Since the snails from Steep Holm were kept together for two and a half years before being put in the cage, it is likely that any regional differences in viability, acquired before the experiment was started, will have disappeared during the intervening period. It is thus probable that the correct interpretation of the experimental results is that they reflect real differences in physiological fitness between morphs.

It is clear from Table 1 that the pattern of mortality during August differs from that during the preceding two months. Yellow-shelled snails survived least well (eighty per cent dead) and browns the best (seventy-three per cent dead). The difference in survival between yellows and non-yellows is far short of statistical significance, but the *change* in the proportions of the two classes dying and surviving is nearly significant at five per cent and suggests there has been a change in the direction of selection. August was noticeably cooler than the preceding two months and it is interesting that the trend for yellows to survive better has been halted and possibly reversed. This might have been expected if pink and brown *C. nemoralis* are favoured under cool conditions.

Although the field data from Steep Holm, and the experimental data from Nettlecombe both suggest that selection by climate occurs, it is by no means certain *how* it occurs; in particular it would be interesting to determine whether different shell colours as such confer thermal properties which are sufficiently different to affect the viability of the live snails. Nor is it at all clear that this is the only type of directional selection occurring on the island. Selection due to temperature is undoubtedly only a part of the total selective regime operating on the snails.

Opposite: Shells of Cepaea nemoralis. Left hand column: From Brean Down. Right hand column: From Steep Holm. The larger size of the latter is obvious. From the top of the column the morphs are: yellow five-banded, yellow mid-banded, yellow unbanded, pink five-banded with the bands fused, pink mid-banded, and pink unbanded.

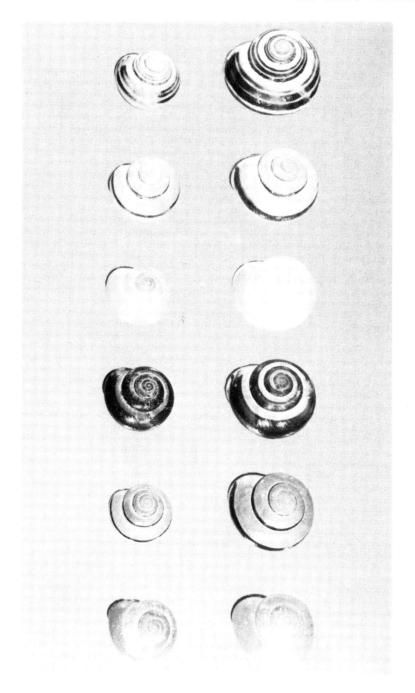

2: *Differences between Steep Holm and the mainland—shell size* The shell of a young snail grows by addition to the edge of the aperture, the calcareous material being secreted from the underlying mantle. When the animal becomes adult there is no further increase in size and a strong ridge, or lip, is formed to strengthen the shell. It follows that there is no association between the age of an adult snail and the size of its shell.

It is clear from even a casual inspection of the shells that *C. nemoralis* on Steep Holm is considerably larger than is usual on the mainland, (Plate II). The usual figure quoted for the diameter of this species is 22.0mm. On Steep Holm the shells are nearly always in excess of this, the largest that has been found having a diameter of 29.0mm.

Variation in shell size is about sixty per cent inherited and differences in fitness conferred by the variation have been studied by a number of researchers. It has been shown that large *C. nemoralis* is more fecund (lays more eggs, more often) than smaller, and that large individuals overwinter better than small ones. These statements relate to laboratory results; neither their generality nor their applicability to the wild are established. Notwithstanding this, it is worth asking, not why are the Steep Holm snails large, but why are the mainland ones small?

Darwin was the first to draw attention to the larger size of some prey species on islands and suggested that the absence of predators was the cause. There are many predators of *Cepaea;* the most important of these is the song thrush which hunts by sight. Thrush-anvils are a common sight in many parts of Britain and predation is sometimes very heavy—several hundreds of snails can be destroyed by only a few thrushes in several days.

Other predators of *Cepaea* are rabbits, rats, bank voles, hedgehogs, badgers and shrews. A striking feature of the Steep Holm fauna is the scarcity of the vertebrate predators of snails. The song thrush is rare—only a few pairs nest each year—and predation from this source is very slight. For example in 1972 only sixteen thrush-broken snails were found out of a total of 1,091 snails observed. Results from other years are consistent with this.

Additionally, there are no rodents on Steep Holm and the rabbit is not particularly common. It seems reasonable to suggest that large size has evolved on Steep Holm at least in part because of the scarcity of important predators, and it seems equally reasonable to search for evidence that the song thrush does actually select for shell size. Ideally the evidence should consist of a demonstration that thrushes remove larger snails from natural colonies. Such evidence has never been obtained, not because this is impossible but because it would be extremely time consuming.

When a thrush hammers a snail on a stone the central column fractures so that the shell breaks across the whorls, the aperture remaining undamaged. It follows that the maximum diameter of a shell cannot be measured after it is broken in this way. It would thus be necessary to measure a large number of snails in different colonies and unique-mark them with drill holes next to the lip so that the mark can be subsequently interpreted.

An additional complication is that mean shell diameter can vary between colonies which are close together and care would have to be taken to ensure that the thrush-broken shells were compared with those of live snails from the same colony (perhaps only a few metres in extent). Predation of snails by thrushes is not a very predictable event and it would be necessary to mark thousands of snails in many different colonies in the hope that predation would occur on a few of them. Notwithstanding these difficulties, the attempt should be made.

There is some evidence that thrushes can select for shell size in experimental populations. In collaboration with J.A. Bayley the author has carried out two experiments at Nettlecombe using mixed populations of *C. nemoralis*. In each case the larger species was preferred, and there was a slight sign of selection *within* species. It is possible to argue that behavioural differences between species and size classes rendered one type more conspicuous to thrushes, rather than that selection on size as such occurred.

A procedure whereby empty shells are "baited" with bread has recently been devised by P. Harvey. He has found that thrushes sometimes take these readily and that when a choice between two size classes is available they take the larger. The experiments using live snails and baited shells both give results interpretable in the same way, so that it is distinctly possible that the large size of *Cepaea* on Steep Holm is related to the scarcity of the thrush.

It is however, by no means certain that this is the only explanation. In a population cage experiment recently carried out at Nettlecombe, R.W. Knights using a design that allowed differences in fitness to be detected between snails collected as close together as five metres, found that larger individuals of *C hortensis* survived better than smaller ones in cages which were sheltered from the sun, the converse being true for exposed cages. The experiment has not been repeated for *C. nemoralis,* but it is interesting to point out that larger *C. nemoralis* are found on the north facing slope of Steep Holm compared with the southern slope. The result illustrates the difficulty of making complete interpretations of biological variation; environmental pressures due to temperature variation will be quite different from those due to the presence of predators.

The foregoing account has been concerned with relative differences between populations, either between populations on Steep Holm itself, or between Steep Holm and the mainland. Changes in morph frequency and shell size represent adaptive micro-evolutionary responses to directional selection. Small changes of this kind can occur without the incorporation of new genetic material, but it is clear that such material will be required for any substantial evolutionary change. Changes which increase fitness in a given place will be favoured. If the population in which they occur becomes spatially isolated the genetic make-up may eventually diverge so far that should the population subsequently require contact with others, the production of viable offspring may be impossible.

In other words a new species has appeared. It is generally held that geographical isolation is a necessary stage in animal speciation since without it migration between potentially diverging populations would "even out" genetic differences.

Genetic changes occur in different ways. For example, hemophilia in man results from a gene mutation but mongolism results from a numerical change to the chromosome complement. Between these extremes lie visible changes to *parts* of the chromosomes. If a chromosome breaks twice and the three pieces rejoin with the central segment inverted, the *order* of the genes will have been changed. Inversions have been of importance in the evolution of new races and species in both animals and plants. The reason for this is that the viability of an organism is affected by the relative positions of the genes; an inversion changes these and this affects fitness.

An individual which possesses an inversion of one chromosome but not on the other of the pair in question (the chromosome complement is made up of pairs, one number of each pair having been donated from each parent) may find it difficult to form gametes, but not if both chromosomes have the inversion. Thus any advantage of the inversion must more than offset this initial disadvantage. Genetic changes of this kind are more likely to become established in small isolated populations with low migration rates than in large ones, because all the individuals can more quickly come to possess the new arrangement on both chromosomes.

Isolating mechanisms between populations vary. They range from behavioural (failure of individuals from different populations to mate) to cytogenetic (failure of hybrid offspring to develop or reproduce).

Cepaea nemoralis has a low migration rate; it is unlikely that animals found more than forty metres apart will ever meet, and the effective breeding colony may be much smaller than this. The opportunity for different *Cepaea* populations to acquire genetic differences leading eventually to inter-population sterility is considerable. Although the formal breeding programmes with *Cepaea* suggest that snails crossed from different places are able to produce fertile offspring, the experiments have been necessarily artificial in that a *choice* of mating partner has not been available. There are no comparative data available relating to possible differences in fertility and viability of offspring derived from inter-population crosses; this is a field that would be well worth investigating.

C. Page has recently shown that there is a chromosomal difference between Steep Holm's *C. nemoralis* and this species from the mainland of West Somerset. This is the first time variation of this kind has been found in *Cepaea*. The difference involves an inversion and may be sufficient to effectively isolate the two populations even if they were given the opportunity to meet. This has yet to be done. Hybrids between the two populations may prove to be sterile (since they will possess unlike chromosomes for the relevant pair), and thus have the status of 'mules'. In which case *C. nemoralis* on Steep Holm is a different species from that on the mainland.

It is of interest to point out that there are a number of differences between the shells of Steep Holm and mainland *C. nemoralis,* in addition to those relating to size. The bands in banded snails are broader than in most mainland snails, and are frequently less 'clean' in outline. The positions of the fourth and fifth bands are displaced downwards so that the area without pigment on the lower surface is consequently reduced in size. In unbanded shells there is frequently a flush of lilac pigment in the whorl immediately adjacent to the lip; this feature does not occur in most mainland populations. It will be of special interest to determine whether the chromosomal rearrangement is related to these shell changes.

This resumé of *Cepaea nemoralis* on Steep Holm raises more questions than it answers. It is clear that the species differs from mainland populations in both absolute and relative ways (chromosome structure and shell size).

The precise adaptive significance of the former is unknown but presumably reflects an evolutionary response to the unusual conditions on the island. The large size of the Steep Holm snails may be related to chromosomal reorganisation, to a reduction in predation intensity, or microclimatic conditions, or to all three of these. Evolutionary problems are solved by compromises. If for some reason, large shell size is desirable on Steep Holm why are not the snails even bigger? What are the factors which determine the upper and lower limits of shell size?

The same general question can be asked of the colour polymorphism. Temperature differences are implicated in the strong variation with aspect on Steep Holm, but why do the populations remain polymorphic? Does the persistence of the polymorphism represent any adaptive strategy enabling a population to cope with variable conditions, and not just with one type of environment?

The study of the Steep Holm snails shows how intricate are the evolutionary changes which a species may make when adjusting to different environments. *C. nemoralis* on Steep Holm serves to remind us of the complexity of living systems, and of the difficulties in interpreting animal populations.

Acknowledgement   It is doubtful if the work described in this paper would have been carried out had it not been for the help of Kim Noble and Michael Ratsey. I am most grateful to them both. Further reading: R.J. Berry *Inheritance and Natural History,* in the New Naturalist series, Collins 1977. *Editor's note:* Dr. Bantock is with the Department of Biology and Geology at the Polytechnic of North London, and his work on Steep Holm is supported by the Science Research Council.

The man and the island

John Fowles

SOMETHING STRANGE happened to me on the day of Kenneth Allsop's death. I was driving round France with my wife, and about three o'clock that afternoon we stopped in the little town of La Rochefoucauld to look at the famous chateau there. But as we crossed the bridge over the river that runs in front of it, something caught my eye.

It was a swift, hanging suspended from some high telephone wires over the water. There were boys fishing and the bird must have taken a fly off the end of one of their lines. The hook was in its gullet, the gut somehow wrapped round the wires. There was absolutely no way to rescue it. Repeatedly the poor creature flapped, winnowed a frantic foot or two up, then fell again and was jerked to a stop.

Out of nowhere the thought of Ken drifted into my mind: how I would have to tell him about this when we returned home, how he was one person who would feel the same acute distress that we did. A week later, in another part of France, I picked up an English newspaper and for the first time learnt that at that precise hour of that same May day during which I had watched the swift in its last lonely agony, Ken also had been dying in his Dorset mill.

In one way it was his misfortune to be so well-known on the television screen, since that side of his career came to overshadow an aspect of his life that was much closer to his heart. Ken didn't merely observe nature, he felt it—felt it with empathetic passion and also, in his last years, with a mounting despair at man's selfishness and greed. At least part of the despair was a by-product of his countless public battles for good conservation causes; in the end he was becoming a sort of unofficial ombudsman in this field. From all over Britain, anyone with an environmental problem tried to enlist his support.

Opposite: Kenneth Allsop speaking with courage and conviction, to a bank holiday audience at Tyneham in Dorset. He railed against the arrival of west Dorset oil explorers.

Of course he made enemies. When he was trying to save a unique bog-oak wood in Dorset from coniferization, one well-known local society withdrew their support on the ground that "it does not pay to offend the Forestry Commission". That was not Ken's way. Where saving nature was concerned, he was prepared to offend everyone in sight. It may not be the best technique on all occasions; but we can ill spare public figures with his courage and conviction in these matters.

Not an easy man to match, when it comes to finding a memorial . . . it was originally planned to buy part of Eggardon Hill, near his Dorset home. But although that would have been entirely appropriate on sentimental grounds—it was his favourite walking and birdwatching place—it lacked the kind of challenge he was always so ready to meet himself. It was already reasonably safe from exploitation. And this is how the island of Steep Holm enters the story.

Steep Holm is that sveltely abrupt hump out in the Bristol Channel which seems to have wandered in from another, more tropical, latitude—an impression some of its characteristic flower species do not contradict when one actually lands. Wall pellitory, that ubiquitous Mediterranean plant, springs from every cranny; so also in some places do the long stems and pink stars of the tree mallow. Geologically the island is an outcrop of Carboniferous lime-stone and its cliffs show the same strata that are exposed in the Avon Gorge at Bristol. Its plateau top extends to some fifty varied—there is even a small wood of sycamores—acres. The nearest mainland is the point of Brean Down, three and a half miles away.

Steep Holm in the middle of the last century. This engraving published by A. Shrowle shows the island's boathouse, inn and cliffside cottage. Close to the top there is a lookout, and on the summit a flagpole.

The island has a long human history, going right back to Saxon and Viking times. It was first permanently occupied in the 12th century, when a short-lived priory (only partially excavated) was founded there; but rather less holy inhabitants— pirates and smugglers—seem to have taken over for the next five hundred years. Then in 1832 a new owner had a farm built and for almost a century Steep Holm was sparsely inhabited: by the farmer, occasional fishermen and gatherers of sea-bird eggs—the latter being then used in sugar-refining. In its heyday the island even boasted an inn—now, along with the three or four cottages, in complete ruin. But the great Victorian event for Steep Holm was the decision to turn the island into a "stone frigate" during the 1860s. Six elegant batteries and a small barrack building were built; the massive Parrott guns and 18th century cannon from some earlier defence system still lie on the ground awaiting resurrection. More modern—and alas, far uglier—emplacements were added during the 1939—45 War. No one has lived on the island since then and it has reverted to wilderness.

Steep Holm, in its military rôle. An elegant battery, called Tombstone, dates from 1868 and the island's "stone frigate" days.

Famous, and beautiful, the May bloom of Paeonia mascula is seen nowhere else in the British Isles.

And what is Steep Holm like to visit? It is first of all a magnificent gazebo, with superb views of the Somerset coast and Exmoor on one side, and of the Welsh sea-board and mountains to the north. But it also possesses a strange inward quality, a kind of haunted isolation that visitors seem to have felt ever since the 18th century. It is not only the elder-choked cottage ruins, the Victorian military relics, all the still visible traces of former human occupation; not even the reputed presence of a ghostly prior or the better attested existence somewhere on the island of a huge cave called "the Church", but I think above all, and especially to the natural historian, this quality of strangeness lies in the island's very peculiar ecology.

Botanically it is dominated by introduced plants, and ancient evidence suggests that some of the introductions may date back as far as the 12th century priors. The characteristic undergrowth is formed of elder, privet and a plant called alexanders. This last was widely grown in the Middle Ages as a pot-herb—it has a remote (very remote, to my palate) similarity to celery. It now forms a summer mini-forest all over the flatter expanses of Steep Holm, alternating in places with stands of hemlock, another important plant in the mediaeval herbal pharmacopoeia. Two other common plants on the island, henbane and the wall pellitory, may be present there for the same reasons. But the most famous of all the escapes from the former priors' garden is the wild peony *Paeonia mascula*.

Steep Holm is the only British station for this superb species, whose natural habitat is confined to southern Europe. It has deep-pink single flowers, some four inches across; and by some miracle of survival it has managed to seed itself down

John Fowles (standing) on a wildlife quest along the southern cliffs of Steep Holm, pointing out the site where the ravens used to breed.

the centuries. Peony-root was once an important anti-spasmodic, used in epilepsy (Gerard prescribed it against nightmares), and perhaps the priors drove a local trade in simples. More certainly the peony has survived because of *unstable* soil conditions—not the reverse, as one might think. The same holds for the island's other plant rarity, the wild leek *Allium ampeloprasum.*

For the non-botanist, easily the most memorable species on Steep Holm is the herring gull. The island now shelters one of its largest English breeding colonies, 'servicing' both sides of the Bristol Channel. When I was there in June, there were areas where one could hardly take a step without threatening to crush eggs or chicks. A population this size—up to 30,000 if you include the young as well—is a magnificent spectacle . . . though not one it is advisable to watch bare headed, since frightened birds do not suffer from constipation. There are attendant colonies of great and lesser blackbacks. The only other cliff-breeding seabird now present is the cormorant. However, fulmars have come prospecting and guillemots and razorbills are recorded from the past. Some blame the gulls for their disappearance, but it seems more likely that the turbid tidal conditions round Steep Holm never afforded a good auk station. Birds from Lundy Island are still seen fishing nearby, so all hope may not be lost. Gannets and Manx shearwaters are also frequent passers in summer, and the occasional seal. The island's only land mammals are the rabbit and hedgehog; there is not a single rodent—a remarkable ecological blank. Rodent carcases are quite common, but they have been brought by the gulls from the mainland. Among bats, only the pipistrelle has been recorded, but other species may be present.

One pair of peregrines and one of ravens used to breed regularly, but the arrival of the Army garrison seems to have driven them away in the first place, and pesticides did the rest. If, outside the herring gull, the breeding list is not very long, there are great hopes that the migrant and casual list will one day be very different. The island is an obvious stage on the western migration route and this aspect of its life has never been consistently observed. In 1974 alone three new species were added to the previous tally.

I must mention one last very odd denizen of the island: the purse-web spider *(Atypus affinis)*. For a long time this creature (one of the large British species) posed scientists an insoluble problem. Its web is a silk tube closed at both ends. The spider lives inside, apparently totally self-excluded from the outside world. So how can it catch its prey? Its secret is now known. When a fly lands on the tube, the spider creeps along inside, then strikes with its specially adapted fangs through the silk envelope, rather as Hamlet killed Polonius behind the arras. It has also evolved a special cutting-tooth, which makes a little slit in the fabric. The fly is dragged through the slit, and that is that; though like a good housewife *Atypus* always 'darns' the slit before it sits down to its meal.

It may seem to be paradoxical, but what most attracted the Kenneth Allsop Memorial Trust to Steep Holm were its problems as well as its natural charms and assets. Over the years it has become something of a Cinderella. The Army left the

Above: Television being used the way Kenneth Allsop would have wished—reporting on a team from the International Voluntary Service clearing wartime debris from the island's main path.

Opposite: Steep Holm, svelte but ecologically rich and important, seen from its eastern approaches. To the right of the beach stands the ruins of a 19th century inn. The cliffs support a dense sycamore wood.

usual rusting mess behind when they retired in 1946 and there is a formidable amount of clearing-up to be done; there are problems of access in some weathers; though there is cistern water for human beings, there is no dependable open water for small birds.

There are delicate problems of gull control and habitat improvement—matters on which the Trust will place themselves under the aegis of the British Trust for Ornithology and the Nature Conservancy.　Fortunately the 1867 barrack building still stands, though it urgently needs further repair; in time it could become an excellent Field Study Centre.

Thanks to a warm and widespread public response to the appeal for funds, the Kenneth Allsop Memorial Trust was able to purchase Steep Holm in 1976. Although, like every charity, we have suffered a little from the general hard economic times, and still lack the funds to do much that we should like, considerable progress has been already made on a number of essential tasks. Many willing volunteers have come forward to help with the cleaning up and the restoring of the batteries, on which a start has now been made; and we have benefitted from the visits of many naturalists. The Management Committee now has the experience and expertise of such well-known Westcountry naturalists as Dr Ernest Neal and Mr Tony Parsons to call on; and we are especially grateful to the latter for the ringing and general field-work he has done on the island. However, most gratitude must be expressed for the honorary secretary of the Trust, and author of this book, Rodney Legg. He has not only shouldered virtually all the day-to-day administration but also supplied a constant flow of enthusiasm and new ideas for the island's future. He has been our dynamo, and I do not know what we would have done without him. But I do know that Kenneth Allsop would have shared these feelings—and delighted in seeing the essence of his own spirit so well perpetuated in another journalist and fighter for conservation.

In Rodney Legg's book the island's varied ecology is explained in the context of its unusual history. It does nothing to lessen the romantic appeal of the island to submit its life to examination and research. If anything, it is only on such a pre-cisely defined piece of land, brought into a sense of proportion by its isolation, that we can begin to understand the complex inter-relationships that shape nature every-where. Knowledge does not reduce romance, but replaces the illusion with the stimulus of constant change and discovery. To understand and appreciate is only the first stage. In these sad times a love of nature—as Kenneth himself so often pointed out—is empty if it is not also a will to safeguard and protect it.

Steep Holm is a small island, but an ecologically rich and important one; a war-scarred island, but a fundamentally beautiful one; an island at present locked away, but one that many would grow to love if they knew it. Let me put it very simply: it needs us, and we need it.

Kenneth the naturalist

Betty Allsop

I DO not know how old my husband was when his love affair with wildlife began. Sometimes I think it must have started while he was still in the perambulator. It was surely inborn since he was an only child and neither of his parents shared his interest although they did not discourage it. However, I do know that his love of birds was deeply established by the time he could write because I have some nature notes written in a seven-year-old's scrawl and there are bird-sighting references in early Lett's Schoolboy's Diaries of his that have survived.

Although born in Yorkshire, Kenneth grew up in one of the hideous ribbon developments on the western outskirts of London, and much of his bird-watching was done in Osterly Park, not infrequently unashamedly trespassing. As he grew older and was able to cycle his expeditions took him further afield, most often to Staines gravel pits. To his later shame and regret he indulged in egg-collecting during his boyhood and when he joined the Royal Air Force in 1940 he presented his collection to the Heston and Isleworth Borough Museum, although whether they were displayed, destroyed or just languish there I do not know. His childhood 'crimes' were to some extent mitigated by the round-the-clock watches he organised to protect the eggs of rarer birds nesting near his home.

The little I know about birds I learned from Ken, but my knowledge is patchy and somewhat odd. Since he knew all the listed British birds (or so it appeared to me) his excitement flared and his binoculars went up when a rare species caught his eye. The result for me is that I am pretty good at recognising the unusual but woefully ignorant of "the little brown birds" seen every day. Hawks were Kenneth's greatest love and he himself had the piercing eyes of a falcon.

I have some knowledge of his childhood habitat for after we were married I was taken on a Bird-watcher's Wife's equivalent of the Victorian's Italian tour— gravel-pits, marshes, moors, woodlands—and I learned *never* to move, and to speak only in a whisper. On one occasion when we were living in Hertfordshire we were walking through some woods and Kenneth felt sure that the Nightjar (a bird he had never seen) must inhabit the area. So about a week later, towards sundown, we set off for the forest and settled ourselves on a fallen tree in a small clearing and waited for Thomas Hardy's "Dew-fall Hawk".

Sharp, knotty bumps dug into my bottom, mosquitoes ambled over my hands, face and neck feasting themselves, but my one attempt to brush away a particularly vicious beast brought a violently hissed "don't move" and we sat on silently waiting, unconscious of time. Then came the unmistakeable call of the male and we saw our first Nightjar; then another came into view and another and another. It was for me a tremendously exciting moment and for Ken an almost unbearably exquisite happiness. We watched them wheeling and gliding and listened to their churring song and it was quite dark when we left the wood.

I cannot write about my husband without acknowledging his debt to Henry Williamson. Although he had several bird-watching companions Kenneth's feeling of identification with birds imbued him with a sense of isolation. Then at about 12 or 13-years-old he casually picked up in the local public library a book entitled *The Lone Swallows*. He idly opened it and began to read. The effect on Ken I quote here from his own notes: "I experienced a confusion of excitement, wonder, disbelief and, almost fear. For the first time I had encountered someone who, it seemed, felt as I inarticulately and gropingly did about birds and the countryside.

"In the dim light of that library I read on, through sketch and short story and essay, enchanted and dizzy with discovery and when I was tapped on the shoulder and told that the library was closing I walked still dazed, with the book held tight, home through the winter evening to the quiet of my bedroom and to start again, more slowly, to assimilate the marvel of the day."

During the following months he gorged himself on Williamson's books and in his imagination lived in Williamson country, walking the Devon lanes, wandering over the Burrows and watching the Peregrine from the cliffs. That visit to the library laid the foundation of a long, affectionate relationship, which, with one or two breaks, lasted until Kenneth's death.

Our honeymoon was spent in Henry Williamson's North Devon when I was shown where the Peregrine used to be, but alas is no longer.

Ken and I met during the war and within ten weeks we were married. Only months later he injured his knee while on battle-course training and in 1945 emerged from two years in hospital minus a leg but with a determination not to permit this loss to curtail his mobility. Even during his time in hospital he pursued his hobby whenever possible and on some days when the weather was good enough and he was well enough I would push his wheelchair to a nearby common where he would relax with his binoculars.

After his discharge from hospital and while awaiting an artificial leg, he became very mobile on crutches and on a convalescent holiday that we spent on the Yorkshire moors, we walked many miles on bird-watching expeditions. We climbed too. Kenneth would manage alone for most of the climb but as we neared the peak and the hill steepened, I would place my head in the small of his back and together, he with his crutches flying, me as a kind of rear-wheel drive, we would race to the top and collapse breathless and laughing on the ling. We must have presented an extraordinary picture.

In 1946 he returned to the *Slough Observer* where previously he had been a trainee reporter. From here he was able to explore many of his old bird-watching haunts and in 1947 he helped to found what has since become the very valuable authoritative and respected Middle Thames Natural History Society. He edited the Society's first report and, young and obscure as he and the society were both, asked James Fisher to write the introduction, a request to which Mr Fisher most kindly acceded.

In the discoloured pages of an old exercise book marked on the cover "Journal, 1947" there is this entry: "Sat. May 31: With the Society to Ham Fields. First sight of Little Ringed Plover: perched on grass spit. We crept along in the shelter of the bank to obtain closer view. It took to wing: small, fawny-brown bird without the white wing-bar of the Ringed Plover. Another joined it. The second bird made a wide circle and landed in the square cultivated field adjoining the water. It ran along a furrow and squatted. We could not hope there might be a nest but after watching it for a time it rose and we walked across. In a hollow in the black, shaley earth, without any attempt at a nest, four eggs—smaller than the Ringed Plover's and very finely speckled with liver-brown on a khaki background. A harrow in the corner—will it be used before they hatch?"

Sadly it was and the nest was destroyed. Nevertheless this was the first breeding record of the Little Ringed Plover for Berkshire, and was the germination of his lovely and prize-winning novel *Adventure Lit Their Star*.

His career was now moving in directions he wanted. By the time he was thirty-

The piercing eyes of a falcon: Kenneth Allsop on the balcony of his mill-house home at West Milton in the Dorset hills. From here he watched the teeming bird life of the valley.

25

years-old he had had two books published and had joined the staff of *Picture Post*, a long-cherished ambition. He was later to join at its outset Independent Television News although his stay there was very brief, and after working on occasional television series—ABC's The Bookman, Granada's Searchlight and others—he joined the BBC in 1960 and remained with them until his death in 1973. He never gave up working for newspapers, remaining primarily a writer and after the death of *Picture Post* he spent some time with the *Evening Standard*, before beginning a long association with the *Daily Mail*, for many years as literary editor and later as a regular contributor.

Despite his heavy work-load, which in general comprised daily television appearances, weekly newspaper columns and books in the pipelines, Ken still somehow found time to engross himself in the British countryside which for him was the essence of living. But from very early on his interest had developed beyond the joys of bird-watching and he had become concerned with ecology. An approach he made in 1948 to the local council on behalf of the Slough Natural History Society resulted in Ham and Slough sewage farms becoming bird sanctuaries, and a glance at his writings from then onwards reveals a growing anxiety about the threatened countryside and a realisation of the need of a well-managed conservation policy.

He was already aware that, as Dr. E. F. Schumacher wrote in his invaluable book *Small is Beautiful*: "Modern man has built a system of production that ravages nature and a type of society that mutilates man." In Ken's files one continually comes across memos to editors suggesting articles on endangered species, endangered hedges, endangered landscapes; though it would seem that not too many of his suggestions were taken up. He was ahead of his time and ecology was not a fashionable word then.

Later of course he became famous as a conservationist through his *Sunday Times* This Britain column and his television programme Down to Earth, and as a private citizen he was involved in many campaigns. As a result of all these activities he became the focus for individuals and groups throughout the country. Every day his post was weighted with letters seeking advice and support and although his time was so full and he was so overworked he tried to answer every letter and to help whenever he could.

Although perhaps his name is most closely linked with the battle to protect West Dorset against the oil drills, the saving of about 200 acres of primeaval oak forest below Eggardon Hill which had been scheduled for Forestry Commission clear-felling does, I think, best illustrate his dedicated purposefulness and untiring staunchness. Day after day, after day, he badgered and bullied the Forestry Commission officials at regional and national level, bombarding them with letters and telephone calls.

Finally, he met them on the site and pursued his argument without pause throughout the better part of the day. As a result the Dorset Naturalists Trust was presented with more than 100 acres. It is a tribute to Ken's vision and knowledge and determination that today Powerstock Common has become the Dorset Trust's showpiece nature reserve and the experts flock there; and it is a memorial to Kenneth and the power of the individual to overcome apathy and indifference. Ken drew the moral himself: "It is not enough to assume that all action can be safely left to the appointed custodians—because not infrequently it may be discovered too late that there has been no action. The individual's vigilance has never been so vitally important." And, as he showed, sometimes capable of success.

Indifference to the pollution of rivers, the rape of the countryside—the designation "Area of Outstanding Natural Beauty" does not necessarily bestow protection—the litter with which we befoul the fields and woodlands and cities: disinterested acceptance of all this and more as inevitable and unalterable enraged him.

On one occasion he was driven to attempt direct action when we were visiting Edinburgh and saw a caged Kestrel. The effect on heaven of Blake's caged Robin was tranquillity compared with the fury that possessed Ken. Nothing would satisfy but to break open the cage and release the bird and I was enrolled to search for some object that would serve as a jemmy. Being a timid soul and cringingly law-abiding I tried reason and remonstrance. I have to admit that what was also concerning me was fear of publicity. Newspaper headlines were racing through my mind; "TV man held bird" in the *Sun*, "English Rector of Scottish University jailed" in *The Scotsman*. However although my pleas were ignored Ken's rescue operation was defeated by our inability, despite much searching, to find a chisel, a hammer or even an adaptable stone so once again his weapon was his typewriter and he wrote a very critical article of the administration of the zoo.

Not all his time was spent fighting and not all his writing was incursive. He had a lovely sense of humour which is frequently to be found in the *In The Country* columns he wrote for the *Daily Mail* (a collection published in hardback by Hamish Hamilton and paperback by Coronet). He derived a great deal of enjoyment from writing them and immense pleasure from the many letters that arrived unfailingly every week. If his battles with authority made him notorious it was clear from his post that his *In The Country* articles made him much-loved. There were letters from people living in rural communities who recognised much that was part of their everyday lives: a regular correspondence developed with some of them and each year he would receive the first spring flowers from Cornwall and from Wales from kindly and appreciative readers. Perhaps though the greatest number of letters came from deprived urban areas; from people who had lived all their lives in cities and had never known the countryside at first-hand, and from those, many now old, who had grown up in the country but who now lived in industry-grimed tenements and back-to-backs and for whom the articles revived happy childhood memories.

Kenneth and I were in Wales the weekend before he died where we were lucky enough to see Ravens, Buzzards, Kites and, most important of all, Peregrines. The entry in his diary for 20 May 1973 reads "A red letter day. Drove with RSPB warden to only Peregrine eyrie in . . . . . Almost as soon as we parked and climbed over heap of scree to little watching bay, the falcon and tiercel were aloft ringing—as were two Kites and two Buzzards, and also a Kestrel! All morning there with magnificent views of birds singly and simultaneously (size difference then very marked) gliding and ringing, and also three times in stoops—in sport, on to passing Kestrel and casual attack on some pigeons. A magical day."

In his more extended notes about that day he wrote: "We poison them, we shoot them, we steal their eggs and their young. It is so wrong. We are the predators and the killers, not those Peregrines. For they and the few of their kind which survive live exalted lives, true to their nature, and we degrade and damage their world which is so beautiful and complex and balanced."

It was encouraging to hear in October 1977 that those Peregrines in Wales have managed a successful breeding season. And how right it is that the Peregrine has now become a constant visitor to Steep Holm, bringing excitement and delight to naturalists—and a hope for the future that Ken, in 1973, was unable to share.

Kenneth Allsop is buried beneath a young medlar tree, moved from his own garden, in the country churchyard of Powerstock near Bridport, in west Dorset.

Vikings and monks

Rodney Legg

HISTORY, FOR Steep Holm, begins with legend and folklore as it does in all lands. There is a mythical monster in the form of the Giant of Gorm. He fights with Vincent, Lord of Avon, for possession of the countryside, but is defeated. Gorm trips as he flees and the dirt from his spade becomes Maes Knoll, an outcrop at Whitchurch, south of Bristol. The giant himself falls flat into the Bristol Channel and drowns, his bones forming the islands of Steep Holm and Flat Holm and the headland of Brean Down.

Less fancifully, another longstanding tradition associates the British monk and historian Gildas with the island. John Leland, King Henry VIII's antiquary, had access to manuscripts which have since been destroyed and he quotes one document as saying that Gildas and Cadocus, another Welsh Saint, retired to two islands between the English and Welsh coasts, Cadocus to the one near Wales, and Gildas to that near England. The islands are not named in the original document but Leland gives them as Ronnet (or Romuth) and Echin (or Echni) which can be translated as Steep Holm and Flat Holm respectively. There can be little doubt about the identity of the two islands, as no others have a dual relationship with the Welsh and English coasts. The Celtic prefix *ro* (the Welsh *rhy*) implied "great, large" which perfectly describes the way Steep Holm rears up from the water.

Leland goes further than this and says that it was on Steep Holm that Gildas wrote his history of Britain, *Liber Querulus De Excidio Britanniae* (literally, "The book of complaint concerning the downfall of Britain"). Unfortunately, Leland does not give the source of his information, and it has been doubted by subsequent historians. The Dictionary of National Biography states that Gildas began writing in Britanny in 559. If the island tale is a fabrication, the people who might have benefitted from its invention would have been the monks of Steep Holm's 12th century Priory. Associations with a famous saint were always coveted by monasteries and had practical value in encouraging endowments. Such pious lies were commonplace in the early middle ages.

Certainly, the character of Steep Holm would have suited the personality and philosophy of Gildas. He lived between approximately 516 and 570 and having a spell on an island as a hermit was a common monastic practice in the Dark Ages. Being alone probably suited him as he regarded all other humans as unrighteous. It is tempting to think that the mental disorder now known as "lighthouse-keeper madness"—which occurs when men are put alone on islands—may explain the content of his writings. Unfortunately it is outrageously unlikely. Steep Holm is clearly visible from Glastonbury Tor, 22 miles away, and as such must have been an obvious candidate as a place of solitude, for monks to show how holy they were. Gildas may well have gone to Steep Holm, and thought out his philosophy during this period, but he could not have written the manuscript on an island. Writing was a complicated business in the 6th century and only a well-equipped abbey like Glastonbury would have been suited for it, with the necessary parchments, ink and pens.

The most likely explanation is that Gildas lived on Steep Holm for his first period of chosen solitude, probably about 540, which would coincide with the monastic apprenticeship of Cadocus, who later founded Llancarvan monastery. At the age of about 33, in 549, Gildas left England—probably from St Illtyd's monastery—for Brittany and spent the rest of his life at Ruys near Vannes. He did not start writing until he had been in Britanny ten years.

Known as "Saint Gildas the Wise", he is still on the island at least in spirit. Steep Holm's alleged supernatural phenomenon is the nightly tread of ghostly feet, walking a gravel path that is now gone. This tale has been persistent from Victorian times to the present—or at least if one believes the comments column of the island visitor's book. Mary Collier says in *Ghosts of Dorset, Devon and Somerset* that after living a hermit's life, Gildas returned to Glastonbury: "But although the religious house at Glastonbury was once his home, his ghost haunts Steep Holm. Maybe he loved the little island. He is not seen, but on moonlight nights he is heard nearby the ruin of the Priory, just the slow footsteps of somebody walking along, which are called 'St. Gildas's Tread'."

Gildas came from a strongly eremitical tradition stemming from St. Illtyd and his school in Glamorgan, which evidently had strong Breton links. He is recorded as having spent a time on an island in Brittany called Horata, which makes it a little more likely that earlier in his life he had lived on an island off England. Gildas was Roman by culture and politics, and for all the latter-day descriptions of his writings as the "tiresome wailings of a misery", he is the major historical source for the early 6th century. He was remembered at Glastonbury, where 29 January was set aside as the Festival of St. Gildas Badonicus. Gildas was given other nicknames including the 'Confessor', the 'Albanian', and the confusing 'Elder' and 'Younger' (which came about as it was wrongly thought there were two Gildases).

Viking raiders took refuge on Steep Holm in the summer of 914 and their temporary residence is the earliest confirmed human occupation of the island. A Scandinavian naval attack had taken place earlier that year against Wales and the West in an attempt to outflank King Edward's Saxon army, which was locked in uneasy confrontation with the Danes along an Essex front-line only 40 miles from London.

Steep Holm came into the picture after the fortunes of the western Viking invaders had been reversed by a land battle near Hereford. Two earls, Ohter and Hroald, were the leaders. The latter was killed and Ohter lost his brother in action. A truce was called and the Norsemen "gave hostages (promising) that they would leave the king's domain".

In the summer of 914, the boat belonged not to Frank Watts but the Vikings. Raiders, the remnants of a large Danish fleet, used Steep Holm as a refuge and harried the Somerset coast.

The Danes fell back to the Severn seaboard and looked for an offshore refuge. They chose Steep Holm, though it is probable the island had already been reconnoitred and earmarked at an early stage as a base to withdraw to in the event of failure on the mainland. As Paul Chaillu wrote in his 1889 study *The Viking Age*, the tactics of the Norse fleets "showed considerable boldness and strategical skill, which generally left them with a way of retreat, if necessary, to their vessels or to some island". The Danish fleet, when it arrived in the Bristol Channel, was described as a "great naval force", though the number of ships is not recorded. The total was certainly substantial, reaching three figures, and it is worth noting that in a similar attack on eastern England in 851, 350 Viking longships sailed into the Thames.

From Steep Holm the remnants of the enemy fleet raided the Somerset coast at Watchet and Porlock. In both cases they were repulsed by the Saxon defenders, who were on full alert along the entire coast from Cornwall to Avonmouth. The Danes returned to Steep Holm. The *Anglo-Saxon Chronicle* records: "And then they remained out on the island of Steepholme until they became very short of food and many men had died of hunger because they could not obtain any food. Then they went from there to Dyfed, and from there to Ireland; and this was in the autumn."

The involvement of Steep Holm in this episode would be completely clear except that the version of the Chronicle at Corpus Christi College, Cambridge, names 'Flatholme' as the island the Danes occupied. It is contradicted by the two British Museum versions, both with 'Steepholme', and the manuscript in the Bodleian Library at Oxford also gives 'Steepholme'. So the odds in favour of Steep Holm become three to one. There is supporting negative evidence in that the island's water supply is not mentioned. All four copies of the Chronicle say the Scandinavians left the island because of hunger—which implies the water supply had been adequate. Freshwater trickles down Steep Holm's north-west cliff, even today, but there is no natural water available on Flat Holm.

An accident seems to have happened to the supplies that should have fed the Severn invaders. Such a force did not merely contain troopships, but had full naval support including special vessels, called "vista byrding", carrying provisions. There is no archaeological evidence to throw any light on the expedition. The Chronicle mentions a prison compound near Hereford but it has not been found; neither have battle sites, graves, discarded weapons or any other object.

Somewhere in the Bristol Channel silt there must be Viking swords, and possibly there are the remains of longships under the murky waters. On Steep Holm, even if Viking activity concentrated on the eastern beach, a look-out would have been kept from the top of the island, and somewhere there must be traces that answer to that nebulous description "artefacts".

Steep Holm, in many Somerset histories, is credited with being a refuge for fleeing Saxons in 1067. Certainly, the wives of England's deposed leadership are known to have stayed on an island in the Bristol Channel while arrangements were being made for their exile in Wales. However, the island used for this 'refugee camp' was not Steep Holm but Flat Holm, and the year is more likely to have been 1068. The error comes from a mis-reading of a passage in the *Anglo-Saxon Chronicle* which states: "Gytha, Harold's mother, and many distinguished men's wives with her, went out to Flatholme and stayed there for some time and so went from there overseas to St. Omer".

The earliest dateable remains to survive on Steep Holm are those of its mediaeval Priory, which stood at the eastern end of the island, looking back towards Worlebury and Sand Bay. It was occupied between 1166 and 1260, and possibly for a number of years before and after this period as well. The building was founded as a cell and retreat by Augustinian canons, perhaps from Woodspring Abbey, which stands on the hillside at the north end of Sand Bay. The clifftop Priory on Steep Holm was dedicated to St. Michael, the usual saint chosen for hill sites that poke a proverbial finger towards God, and was given land on the mainland at Uphill, between Brean Down and Bleadon. In 1260 comes the last certain reference to an ecclesiastical building on Steep Holm, when Robert de Tregoz was the patron. He transferred the Priory and its belongings to the control of Studleigh Priory in Warwickshire. They appear to have abandoned the island shortly afterwards, and Tregoz's patronage would have come to an end in 1265, when he was killed in the Battle of Evesham. There is one further mention of Steep Holm Priory, by John Smyth in the late 1500s, saying it was rebuilt by Maurice, Lord Berkeley, in the early 1300s. That may have been the intention, but it seems it was never carried out. John Smyth, in *Lives of the Berkeley family*, writes that "This Lord Maurice (1281-1326) re-built the friary for the fryers and breathren in the Holmes, an Iland in Seavern, and not far from his manor of Portbury". No records, however, have come from any 14th century source to support this statement.

Robert de Tregoz was a member of the de Ewys family, who appear to have made Steep Holm's original endowments. He granted "elemosinam Sancto Michaeli de Stepholm" the "ecclesim Sancti Nicholai de Uppilla"—the early Norman of St Nicholas at Uphill—together with half a virgate (an eighth of an acre) of land there with pasture rights, and use of the mill. The brethren were also given another virgate at Uphill by Robert, and a grant from Thomas de Muncketon "of himself and his land at Curcheston" (Christon).

These charters were sorted out by I. H. Jeayes of the British Museum in the muniment room at Berkeley Castle, Gloucestershire, between 1886 and 1892. The most interesting deed is that of William, Bishop of Bath and Wells, "ordaining that, for the most frequent celebration of divine service at the religious place called Stepholm, with the island which Robert de Tregoz has conferred on the Austin canons of Stodleigh, the Prior shall cause two canons at the least to reside there, the Senior canon to be called the Prior of Stepholme." The Warwickshire priory was in severe debt and Godfrey Gifford, Bishop of Worcester from 1268 to 1302, wrote an undated begging letter asking another Augustinian community in the diocese if they would take care of two brethren for eighteen months. Prebendary E. H. Bates Harbin, who found this letter in the library of Corpus Christi College at Oxford, writes: "One is tempted to surmise that they may be the couple who ought to have been sojourning on the Steepholme". Robert de Tregoz was killed at the Battle of Evesham in 1265. Prebendary Harbin adds "it is now quite evident that Robert de Berkeley was the person who really benefitted by the abandonment of the Priory", but he does not explain how. The only known Prior is William in 1236. He would have lived on the island with a handful of canons, possibly only one or two, so numerically the establishment was not sizeable, though no doubt there would have been paid servants.

As for the inmates, they did not always maintain pure lives, and two lay canons from Steep Holm, Brothers Gregory and Richard, were convicted of larceny by the jury of Winterstoke Hundred in 1243. They were handed back to their Prior for judgement.

The ruins of their building stood "to a height of seven feet, faced with dressed stone of the island" in 1867, but these walls were pulled down for the building of the nearby Palmerstonian gun battery when the military first occupied the island. F. A. Knight writes in his 1902 *Seaboard of Mendip*: "During the construction of Garden Battery, built on the alleged site of the prior's garden, the foundations of the priory were in great part laid bare. One chamber was in such good repair that it was used as living quarters by the foreman. In clearing out the earth to lay a wooden floor the whole space was found to be packed with skeletons laid close together side by side only a few inches below the surface. Nearby, many bones of deer, brass rings of primitive workmanship, a coin with the figure of an archer, as well as many old pieces of money said to show no legible inscription or device were found. There is a tradition that a former tenant of the island dug up a pot of coins, but of them there is no trace now known."

The foundations that survive seem to be from an L-shaped building, with the main wing about 50 feet long by 12 feet wide, and an extension running north at ninety degrees from the east end. Orientation of the main building is west to east. The walls are about three feet thick and have some traces of plaster on the inside. Part of the area was excavated by L. Harrison Matthews and a group of naturalists from Bristol in 1938. They followed the walls to bedrock at a depth of 4 ft. 6 ins. The pottery finds are particularly intriguing, though the attribution of a neolithic date (around 3000 BC) for a coarseware type of pottery is highly dubious and requires scientific verification. This may prove impossible as the shard appears to have been taken to Bristol and lost.

Though there is every reason to think that sailors of the megalithic age paused at Steep Holm while exploring the western seaboard, it would be astonishing for one of their pots to turn up in post-mediaeval levels. Harrison Matthews does not note the context in which this ware was found, and it should be pointed out that much mediaeval pottery completely loses its glaze in normal wet conditions. His report states: "The pottery is very mixed, the oldest fragment being part of the foot of a neolithic bowl. Many pieces of coarse unglazed earthernware, which might be assigned to any date during the last thousand years, were found. With them were associated fragments of buff-coloured mediaeval ware with greenish glaze, 16th and 17th century reeded ware, and shards of modern china. Several pieces of dressed freestone ware were also found, some with dowel holes; these had evidently formed part of the window of an ecclesiastical building, presumably the Priory."

To the north of Priory ruin they found "an area of ground covered with loose stones covering a low mound" which they thought might "represent the dis-integrated ruins of a building". The party did not have time to dig into this and it is now covered by scrub. The concrete base of a Nissen hut lies across the north side of the Priory, but though the outer foundations of the wartime structure will have sliced through the ground, the inner part of its concrete cannot have reached the mediaeval levels. Harrison Matthews noted that the walls of the Priory had been removed to ground level and "not just collapsed inwards". He looked further afield for traces of Priory rubble and found one piece to the north-west: "Built into the wall of the sidearm store of the Tombstone Battery is a piece of a 13th century stone coffin lid or memorial slab of hard blue lias. The edge is moulded and the centre bears part of an incised fleury cross. An inscription on it records that it was excavated nearby in 1867, during the construction of the batteries." This stone has now been removed to the Barracks.

The bones found by the 1938 excavators were animal, including sheep, young oxen, pig, and a horse tooth, but some human remains were found in 1962 when Edmund Mason opened the north-east interior of the Priory. He made the follow-ing notes about these bones: "Part of maxillae of adult containing two molars and two premolars (right side). Only portion of palate of roof remaining shows the grooves for the greater palatine nerve vessels. Interior base of maxillary sinus exposed. One adult middle phalange." Much of the remainder of Mason's material was post-mediaeval and indicates some degree of occupation on Steep Holm in subsequent centuries. The Priory, or part of it, could have been re-used between the time of its desertion and the late 1860s, when it was plundered as an easy quarry for stone. The 1938 dig revealed "a recent hearth of loosely laid bricks surrounded by much ash" and Harrison Matthews pointed out: "Certainly the east wall must have been standing to some considerable height in recent time, for such a hearth would be made only within a building of some sort."

Mason's view was that his potsherds, excepting one or two coarse pieces, were "more recent than the closure of the Priory and would seem to indicate some in-filling during the late 15th century or the first half of the 16th century". He dug to a depth of two feet and thought "that earlier material might be found at a lower level". Little rubble from the building was found, and only two pieces of carved

Still waters off Tower Rock as evening mist envelopes the island. The Flat Holm fog-horn adds to the eerie atmosphere.

stone, which had probably come from a window moulding. In 1975 a visiting archaeologist, Howard Pell, picked up a fragment of hard brown sandstone near Tombstone Battery. It had a nail hole and was part of a stone slate. This was the first clue to the Priory's roofing. It has been identified as a local stone, mainly quarried near Clevedon, known as Pennant slate.

A considerable quantity of human bones were dug from the Priory ruins in June 1977 by a London schoolboy, Diggory Sladden, in an unauthorised excavation. He found the bones, which filled two large boxes, "hard against the inside of the south wall of the Priory" about 16 feet north from its south-east corner. The bones, much jumbled, were a foot below the ground surface. They were from at least nine skeletons, seven being adult males, one a woman and the other a 14-year-old boy. Traditionally, bones have been repeatedly found on Steep Holm. Rev. John Skinner, when he visited the island on 26 July 1832, was told by an old man that when he dug his garden he uncovered a stone vault seven feet long by four feet wide that contained a human skull and skeleton as well as sheep skulls. "Many human bones have been found in this island," a newspaper reported in October 1885. Francis Knight, in *Seaboard of Mendip,* says that when the Priory ruins were robbed of stone during the fortification building of 1868, "it was found that the whole space inside the walls of this building was packed with skeletons, lying close together side by side, only a few inches below the surface". This description matches precisely the discovery made by Diggory Sladden. Perhaps he had found the same spot.

Re-excavation of Diggory's hole was carried out on 19 June 1977 by Colin Clements, and Stan and Joan Rendell. "We are now quite positive that the bones Diggory found were a Victorian re-burial," Stan Rendell said. "Beside the hole, in adjacent undisturbed soil, we quickly found further bones lying in situ. These were a complete jumble and, like those already excavated by Diggory had been damaged and broken at the time of re-burial, before being thrown in a heap." With the bones the excavators found some fragments of a green Victorian beer bottle and a small shard of Willow-type pottery. The bones, they confirmed, were contemporary with the Priory ruin itself, and it is clear that the builders of the 1867 fortifications must have cut through the monks' cemetery. As the tombstone was built into a wall on the north-west side of the Priory, it is reasonable to suppose the cemetery lay at either Tombstone or Laboratory batteries, between the Priory buildings and the northern cliffs. It would, anyway, seem unlikely to have been on the other side of the Priory, as the ground at Garden Battery is the most sheltered on the island and too useful to be sacrificed for burials.

The existence of a Priory on Steep Holm is significant as part of a wider pattern. The *Map of Monastic Britain* shows the sporadic use of islands for outlying cells of abbeys. In south-west England there were offshore establishments at Tresco in the Scilly Isles, Lammana off Looe, and evidence of a hermitage being established by the monks of Cerne Abbas on Brownsea Island in Poole Harbour, though the latter site is not included on the map. In the Bristol Channel region Steep Holm alone has been used for this purpose and there are no signs that monastic as distinct from ecclesiastical occupation took place on either Flat Holm or Lundy. Off the two tips of Wales, monastic houses occur on the islands of Caldy, St Tudwals, Bardsey, and Anglesey together with its offshoots, Holy Island and Puffin Island.

The last site, Puffin Island, has some affinity to Steep Holm in that it too has the plant called Alexanders, introduced by monks as a pot-herb.

Ruined walls on the southern cliffs between the Barracks and South Landing. These are not related to the long field boundaries on the top of the island, but seem to have supported short terraces in a sheltered hollow.

One of the attractions of islands for monks was more practical than religious. Because of the absence of predators, rocks have teeming seabird colonies. For a limited number of people, it would have guaranteed a dependable food supply, all the year round. Puffin, tasting similar to pigeon when fresh, was dried in the sun and kept for the winter. T. C. Lethbridge wrote that the diet of the Westmann Islands, off Iceland, was puffin—for five main meals a week. Having a close and easy food supply would have given the monks the time they required for their meditations and, on Steep Holm, herbal horticulture.

The most fascinating discoveries about Steep Holm's past are yet to be unearthed. In the centre of the island, along the south-facing top from near Summit Battery eastward to well past the Ordnance Survey's concrete instrument post, there are numerous denuded and collapsed field banks, forming a grid-pattern of small enclosures, and some traces of cultivation terraces to the south. Many lines became clearly visible when the 1976 drought removed the vegetation. In the north-west corner of one enclosure, between the Ordnance Survey point and Garden Cottage, there is a rectangle of stones about 20 feet long (west to east) by ten feet across (north to south) open to the field towards the east, and therefore away from the prevailing wind. This small oblong enclosure might have been a pen or shed for stock. It is set in the corners of the main enclosure, but with a six feet gap between its walls and those of the field. A similar small enclosure, a square, is midway between the Barracks and Summit Battery but incorporates larger stones than the field banks. These could be of any date from the Bronze Age to the 18th century, which is a period of four thousand years; even their sizes are no indication of period as farming in any age would have adapted to the constraints of an island. Two parallel banks, about five feet wide by a foot high with a space about nine feet between them, run SSW to NNE across the summit of the island, about 35 feet east of the Ordnance Survey pillar. One extends further than the other and they may well have formed a path between two fields.

The collapsed remains of the longest wall can be followed across the entire length of the island from Laboratory Battery westward, to within sight of Rudder Rock. It was this wall that John Skinner saw in 1832, referring to it as running along the "dorsal" of the island (east to west, that is, though in his notes he mistakenly re-orientates Steep Holm from north to south).

Westward from the ruined Garden Cottage and then southward to a point east of the Barracks there is a square field enclosure which looks later than the other banks and can probably be safely regarded as mediaeval or later, though too collapsed to have Victorian origins. There are so many apparent lines of ancient cultivation and land-use that infra-red photography (giving heat pictures because of the greater warmth of concealed stones compared with untouched earth) may outline the most promising ground for future archaeological exploration.

Piracy must also have a place in the island's history. No other single point in the Severn seaboard has such an uninterrupted vantage of the entire English and Welsh coasts from the open sea to the river estuary. It must have been known to William de Marisco, "a mischievous pirate" who operated from Lundy, and "infested these coasts, in the reign of Henry III".

But perhaps the most striking relic of ancient human occupation lies in something still alive: the island's unique pattern of plant species. This is one of the great surprises that awaits visitors, and deserves detailed examination.

A herbal flora

Rodney Legg

STEEP HOLM has attracted plant-lovers for centuries. Botanically it is one of Britain's best documented sites, receiving attention from William Turner before 1562, and then by others in each subsequent century, culminating with distinguished passages by Geoffrey Grigson in *The Englishman's Flora* in 1958. The most noteworthy visitor, in 1773, was Sir Joseph Banks, the founder of Kew Gardens. Two years earlier he had returned with the first global plant collection, accumulated on Captain Cook's round-the-world voyage in the *Endeavour*. On Steep Holm he picked the Golden Samphire (*Inula conyza*).

Why the island is remarkable, and how it came to be so different from the adjoining mainland, can be explained by analysing its impact on one 19th century visitor. Thomas Clark, a Somerset botanist, was typical of those tempted by the island's fame and he made the trip to Steep Holm in 1831. "I have had for many years the wish to visit this island," he wrote, "principally on account of the rare plants which I know grow there—the piony, the great round-headed garlic, and the caper spurge. We found all there and I have them now planted in my garden."

Despite his takings, and those of other visitors, these three plants still grow on Steep Holm.

One, the Peony (*Paeonia mascula*), occurs as a wild plant nowhere else in the British Isles; its entry in the Cambridge *Flora* admits of no other location. The Collins *Pocket Guide to Wild Flowers* is also specific: "Long naturalised on Steep Holm in the Bristol Channel." The plant has a lushness that betrays its alien, southern European origin, and grows two feet high with a mass of shiny leaves, light green in colour and less divided than those of the garden cultivar. It flowers for scarcely seven days, early in May, with large scented purplish-pink flowers. The main difference between the wild and cultivated varieties is that the Steep Holm flower-heads comprise five to eight single, instead of multiple, petals. Most cultivars derive not from *P. mascula*, but the closely related Asian *P. lactiflora*. Steep Holm's Peony was discovered by F.P. Wright in 1803. This, its earliest recorded appearance, coincided with the Romantic Movement's enthusiasm for the wild beauties of England. Things natural and rural were in vogue, and William Lisle Bowles composed a poem featuring the "abrupt and high" isle of Steep Holm where "desolate, and cold and bleak", on its barren brow, "one native flower is seen". The Peony: "One flower, which smiles in sunshine or in storm . . . sits companionless, but yet not sad."

The second plant attracting Clark—"the great round-headed garlic"—was the Wild Leek (*Allium ampeloprasum*). It is one of the rarest plants of the British western seaboard and was recognised by Clark before his boat had even reached the shore: "The garlic I saw and knew from the boat before we landed, growing abundantly on a high ridge at the eastern end of the island, though I know not that I ever saw it before." Here, below Tower Rock (then called Lion's Head) the Leek was still growing in profusion, amongst clumps of Peony, during the First World War. The oldest reference to the Wild Leek on Steep Holm is an item about a "kind of wild garlicke" in the 1625 account book of the manor of Norton Beauchamp. Today, says the Nature Conservancy, the plant occurs in "few other British localities".

Above: Wild Leek grows below Tower Rock, within sight of the island's landing. The ancestors of this rare cliff-edge plant were found at the same spot by Thomas Clark in 1831.

Opposite: Peonies, leeks and a fragment of tombstone were drawn by T.H. Thomas after an expedition of Cardiff naturalists to Steep Holm on 29th May 1883: "A black-eyed maiden, embrowned by the sun and breezes that breathe and blow around her island home, is charged by the landlady to guide us to the spot where the sacred plant grows."

Text within illustration: EXCAVATED NEAR THIS SPOT 1867

On the top of the island, Clark found both the Peony and his third objective, the Caper Spurge (*Euphorbia lathyrus*). It grows to three feet—in a "highly distinctive, 'architectural' appearance", to use the Collins Guide description. Its leaves are bluish-green and succulent-looking. This plant was the "most used" purgative of John Gerard's famous *Herbal*, its white latex sap the "strong medicine to open the bellie". Though possibly a native of English woods, the plant was more probably introduced into this country for medicinal purposes. Caper Spurge is a rarity as a wild plant, though fairly frequent as a garden weed, mainly because it was widely believed in Victorian times to repel moles. Sir Joseph Banks was the first to record it on Steep Holm. There is no other spot in Britain where it has a recorded history which extends across two centuries.

The other notable plant recorded by Clark was the Alexanders (the confusing 'plural' name applied to single plants is probably a case of a lost apostrophe). Shortly before 1562, William Turner discovered Alexanders (*Smyrnium olusatrum*) in "Ilandes compassed about the sea"; and with this description he was thinking of Steep Holm in particular. It is the most invasive and successful plant ever to reach the island. By May the foliage has reached its full height of five feet and the seedheads have set. In midsummer the plant dies back. By September seedlings are germinating and through mild winters, like 1974-75 when Steep Holm was largely frost-free, nothing slows their growth. They can give the island a rich spring look in the middle of winter. But conditions vary each year. The plants were in a brown, stalky state, "the foliage being nearly decayed", when Thomas Clark made his visit in August 1831. He could bring home only some seeds and roots, but made a useful assessment of their status on the island: "This was very plentiful, I think all over the island; I distinctly recollect it at both ends."

Macgregor Skene, in 1939, described the 'meadow' of Alexanders on the island plateau as "a society which is certainly unique in this country". Naturalised from the Mediterranean, Alexanders grows best above the sea, and in *The Englishman's Flora*, Geoffrey Grigson gives the clue to its distribution: "In England and Ireland you will find it often by the ruins of castles and abbeys." Alexanders was brought to Britain as a pot-herb in the Middle Ages, earthed and blanched, the predecessor of modern celery. Here is the key to the vegetation of Steep Holm. The four species mentioned so far—Peony, Wild Leek, Caper Spurge and Alexanders—have one thing in common.

They were all, and this is nearly a complete certainty, introduced to the island by the Augustinian canons who established the Priory of St. Michael on the edge of the cliffs at the east end of the island. A Nature Conservancy report says about the Peony: "There is little doubt that it was introduced, probably by the monks who occupied the 13th century Priory. In Europe it is similarly associated with ancient monastic establishments." The Conservancy also considers the Wild Leek and

Opposite top: The "architectural appearance" of Caper Spurge, a monkish introduction to Steep Holm, which was first recorded by Sir Joseph Banks in 1733.
Opposite bottom: White flower heads of Alexanders (left) smother the island in early summer. A stem of Greater Mullein (right) has been shredded by Herring Gulls. Ragwort grows at its base.

Caper Spurge to be "probable ancient introductions" to Steep Holm.

Such plants provided the raw materials for the drugs of the Middle Ages and the part abbeys and monasteries played as centres of learning in no way excluded medicine. There is ample historical evidence of their importance as prototype hospitals. For example Professor H.P.R. Finberg in *Lucerna*, a group of studies in early English history, gives details of a property squabble between Glastonbury Abbey and the Norman owner of Uffculme in Devon. This owner arrived at Glastonbury in 1086 to argue his case but fell ill: "He sent three times (to the prior) to beg that he might be clothed in the monastic habit: a very common request in such cases, for if granted it secured for the petitioner skilled medical attention in the infirmary."

John Fowles, chairman of the Kenneth Allsop Memorial Trust and a keen amateur botanist, writes: "Although some speculation is inevitably involved, 20th century visitors to Steep Holm may be fairly certain that a high proportion of the plants they see were once the raw material of a monastic pharmacopeia. No doubt most of the medicine was intended for the members of the order; but a knowledge of simples in an age powerless against disease was plainly an important advantage, both in worldly and Christian terms. The poor could be helped, the rich made suitably grateful."

The island's micro-climate, making it warmer and drier than the mainland, suggests that the Priory may well have been established quite as much for gardening as for religious purposes. The quantity of monkish introductions that survive is evidence of the island's suitability for herb growing and the Priory has left more of substance in its plants than its walls. Even the position of the Priory is indicative of a horticultural intention as it blocks from the north wind an area of ground— traditionally called 'the Garden'—which in a wide variety of conditions is the stillest and warmest place on the top of the island.

In the deeper soil at the Priory there must be quantities of mediaeval pollen, which can perhaps one day be analysed to give a breakdown of the proportions of introduced and indigenous plants, and give firm clues to the extent that the monks affected the island's flora. Meanwhile, visitors to the island can ponder over what John Fowles sees as the probability that Steep Holm's garden meant more to the monks than the Priory building: "So many of the introduced and native plants have important herbal medicine uses that one may plausibly wonder whether the Priory was not regarded more as an extension of the garden of the mother foundation than as a place for solitary contemplation."

Sir Frederick Stern, author in 1946 of *A Study of the Genus Paeonia*, believed the Peony was indigenous only to the centre of France, in the departments of Loir et Cher and the Cote d'Or, and to an area near Reichenhall in southern East Germany. Elsewhere, he thought, it had been introduced by monks. It survives as a wild plant in Cyprus, Sicily, Syria, Steep Holm and northern Soviet Armenia: "In all these places there may have been monasteries in the past, and it is possible these plants are descended from plants growing in the monastery gardens for the medicinal properties credited to peonies in the old herbals." Peonies also used to be found wild in Britain in woods near Winchcombe in Gloucestershire, a place with the same type of historical connections, since it was the capital of Mercia and had a monastery in the 8th century.

Mrs M. Grieve, in her famous *A Modern Herbal*, lists the various healing properties of the key Steep Holm plants. The powdered root of the Peony was used to combat convulsions and epilepsy and was especially efficacious against lunacy. Gerard recommended fifteen seeds in wine or mead against "the disease called the Nightmare". 'Peony water' was a much used mediaeval medicine, and the seeds were advised as a cooking spice as late as 1796. In classical times it was regarded as a plant from the moon, with powerful magic properties, protective of flocks and harvests. Leek is edible, and that speaks for itself. The white oil of Caper Spurge is a violent poison, but was formerly used in minute doses as a strong purgative. The root is equally emetic. The leaf-sap can produce blisters, and was formerly used by dishonest beggars. Alexanders, on the other hand, had no herbal use, but the old herbalists call it the Black Pot-herb, after the colour of the seeds and the specific name—*olus*, a pot-herb, *-atrum*, black. Its former name was *Petroselinum alexandrinum*, in Old French *alexandre*, and hence the common English name. It was much eaten at Lent, apparently because it was regarded as having mildly purging qualities.

Historical accounts of Steep Holm point to a general pattern of vegetation which, while always fluctuating, has changed little overall in the past two hundred years. Starting with the first of the four species detailed in Clark's notes, the current position is that the Peony is still present on the eastern cliffs above the shingle beach (though severely reduced in numbers by a rust disease, caused by the fungus *Botrytis paeonia*). Descendants of the Caper Spurge flourish in a clump of ten plants, on the top of the island, beside the path 30 yards west of the Barracks. A clump or two of Wild Leek is visible from the sea as you approach the South Landing, the plant only being able to compete in cliff-edge associations. Alexanders is as plentiful as ever and covers most of the surface of the island, even growing from rock crevices on the cliffs, much as it does in its more natural Mediterranean habitats. Steep Holm, and to a lesser extent Puffin Island off Anglesey, are the only British sites where the species has become the dominant vegetation.

This dominance can be quantified. On Steep Holm in 1977, Tony Parsons used a calculator and scales to estimate an Alexanders population of 75,000 plants, producing 22 tonnes of seed a year — which represents 450 million individual seeds.

Another numerically significant plant in the past, and still in quantity on the island, is the Privet (*Ligustrum vulgare*). This is the native English species of the Privet, now ousted from suburban hedges by an Asian substitute, the replacement having larger, softer leaves. In Clark's day, Privet was the major Steep Holm plant: "The most abundant, at least the one which occupies the largest spaces, is the common privet which closely covers whole acres." Today it is the principal plant, making a considerable thicket, in the region south-west of the Priory foundations. Though Gerard recommends Privet as a throat gargle, its presence on Steep Holm is much more likely to be because of its value as a hedging plant. The Priory garden would have needed protection from the wind, and Gerard does mention its use as a hedge.

Elsewhere on Steep Holm the primary scrub-plant is now Elder (*Sambucus niger*). The twisted and contorted Steep Holm specimens often stand in superb, craggy situations, but despite appearances the plant does not achieve great age. Elder receives mention, along with Wild Leek and Privet, in the 1625 Norton Beauchamp accounts. Two centuries later, Clark saw only a single Elder bush, "under a rock not far from the well", in the north-east corner of the island. Elder still stands around the same point today, and it was probably from here that cuttings were taken to start shelter-belts alongside stone walls running from the farmsteads into the eastern interior of the island. Ageing Elders grow from ruined walls near Garden Cottage and Priory Farm.

Because of its fast growth, Elder has been used as a hedging tree since ancient times. As with Privet it must have been brought to the island for that purpose, but it also has the advantage of being one of the most useful of all plants. It yields three colours of dye (black, green and purple) and has countless culinary uses (including a pickle from the peeled green shoots) and medicinal ones. The bark is purgative, a fact mentioned by the father of medicine, Hippocrates. The roots are emetic. Ointments of the leaves are emollient and especially good in the treatment of swellings. Elder-flower water is mildly astringent and still used in eye lotion. It was a standard feature of every Victorian lady's dressing-table as a skin cleanser, since it whitens and softens the complexion. In mediaeval times it was also widely used against eruptive diseases like measles and also in treating chest complaints. Various preparations of the fruit—as wine, 'rob', and syrup—have been used at the onset of influenza and to combat other fevers. Throughout Europe the Elder was regarded as the "medicine chest of the poor" and it is probably the single most important species in general herbal medicine.

Cuckoo-pint (*Arum maculatum*) is as noticeable on Steep Holm in the 1970s as it was to Thomas Clark. A food plant of the Middle Ages, its dried tubers were regarded as aphrodisiac, and also used as a substitute for arrowroot. Clark wrote: "The bright coral berries of the cuckoo-pint were in some spots very conspicuous and ornamental, the plant growing not singly or by twos or threes, as on hedge-banks, but in groups of a dozen or more." It is there now in the same profusion, amongst a carpet of ivy, below the central incline of the track sloping up from the beach. An amazing quantity, exceeding a hundred, smothers the shallow earth covering a concrete pad to the north of Cliff Cottage. Cuckoo-pint was a valued though potentially poisonous, medicinal herb. It was formerly used as a violent purgative; and against ring-worm. The roots are edible if properly treated, and were grown for this purpose on the Isle of Portland, under the name Portland Sago or Portland Arrowroot. It was a very common starch in former times, and also had cosmetic uses for women—being said to remove freckles.

"Young plants of henbane I observed on the top of the island," Clark continues, and again their successors are still widespread along the island paths. Henbane (*Hyoscyamus niger*) was the most powerful sedative of British herbal medicine, its leaves providing the alkaloid hyoscine, and juice from seeds "very effectuall in easing the pains of the Teeth". Henbane, a member of the potato family, was familiar in Anglo-Saxon medicine under the name Henbell. A whole mediaeval monastery once supped on the roots in mistake for those of chicory. All entered a delirious frenzy, had hallucinations and behaved like lunatics. It was a favourite constituent of the witches' brew. Useful as a hypnotic and anti-spasmodic drug, and as an analgesic, it is highly poisonous, to the extent (visitors be warned) that even the inhalation of vapour from its crushed leaves is dangerous. Curiously its foliage is often pecked down by the island's herring gulls, apparently without harm to them.

Not only have the herbal and monkish introductions established for themselves an integral place in the Steep Holm flora, but there has been a continuity in the general vegetation that has withstood the upheavals of sudden and dramatic change. The war works of 1867 and 1941 caused considerable disturbance, as did cultivation in the farming period of 1910-25, and there were even goats on the island for many years. Steep Holm has evolved a surprisingly unbalanced ecology from a strange admixture of introductions. The status of many of the plants fluctuates with the climate and a species that covers several acres one year can be almost absent the next.

You have to search for the one plant everyone expects to see. Grass, despite the Victorian presence and a come-back in the years following the last war, is once more negligible on Steep Holm as a ground cover plant. In 1949 the Barracks surroundings were grassed but there is now no grass of any consequence, excepting remnants of closely cropped turf appearing as clearings in the sea of Alexanders north and north-east of the Barracks, and on some cliff-edges on the north side of the island. It can in fact survive only where gulls clear away the Alexanders. These

Tree Mallow (left) finds a footing on the exposed island cliffs, bringing a defiant splash of purple to the grey stone. Henbane (right) is not native to the island, but was introduced by the monks who knew it as the most powerful sedative in British herbal medicine.

'gull lawns'–apparently made as landing-strips, since the island has no predators–
are about 80 feet wide but they do not amount to a significant foothold for grass.

Its total area is exceeded nearly three times by that of the Tree Mallow
(*Lavatera arborea*). This is a true maritime species, withstanding gull guano and
gales to bring a defiant splash of purple flowers to the inaccessible top of Rudder
Rock, at the extreme tip of the island. A forest of Tree Mallow smothers the
undercliff east of Split Rock in an acre belt. Even this scrubby plant, like all the
commoner Steep Holm species, had a medicinal role and was used for ointment and
poultices. Tree Mallow leaves steeped in hot water soothe sprains. The flowers can
be used for dyeing.

Tree Mallow is the only colourful plant–the Alexanders flower is white–to be
eligible for inclusion in a survey of the island's ground cover. It is necessary to inject
some statistics into this description, if only to remove any impression of a rocky
island covered with Peony bloom. Nothing, unfortunately, could be less true. The
Peony, and the Wild Leek, are rarities on Steep Holm as well as in national terms.

The predominant vegetation and ground cover, generally, is far more mundane
(though still botanically exceptional) and the following rough breakdown, by per-
centages, was calculated in May 1975, though the situation constantly changes:

Alexanders (frequently understood with Nettle)	59
Elder	11
Scree and rocks	8½
Buildings and concrete	7
Privet	4½
Bramble	3½
Sycamore	3
Tree Mallow	2½
Grass	1

The most recent coloniser in the list is the Sycamore (*Acer pseudoplatanus*),
which covers a large section of the slopes overlooking the beach and has spread
along the cliffs on to the north-east side of the island. There is not a single tree
shown in this area by 19th century engravers. The larger trees were about 25 feet
high in 1954 and are now generally around 30 feet. They seem to have originated
from a deliberate planting, possibly of around two dozen seedlings, in the 1930s,
but taking a 'core' sample from the bigger specimens would be the sure way of finding their age. There are very few saplings amongst the older trees and the wood
does not seem to be extending its edges. The principal belt of trees, incidentally,
lost their leaves in the 1976 drought but the prolonged rains that followed set the
buds sprouting at the end of November, and several trees were covered in young
leaves on 5 December.

Sycamore is the only forest tree on Steep Holm, and the species most resistant
to coastal salt spray and winds–it can live in positions far more exposed than the
east face of Steep Holm. A Sycamore plantation at Castle of May in Caithness is
the most northerly wood in Britain. Appropriately for its Steep Holm ratings, the
Sycamore tree was first brought to Britain from France by monastery gardeners, so
while there is no documentary evidence for its having a long history on the island,

a monastic connection does exist.

Other plants have reached Steep Holm in the last hundred years. One came to the island in the final stages of its well-documented conquest of the stone walls of England's western villages. This plant, Red Valerian (*Centranthus ruber*), grows on Steep Holm in its perfect type-habitat, against the grey background of limestone rock faces, above the cliff track from the beach, and in the cutting behind the Barracks. Few plants can more strikingly enliven a bleak piece of scenery. The species was probably introduced to British gardens from southern Europe in the sixteenth century, and not until the 1770s had it spread to the "old tumbledown walls" of the West Country. By 1891 it had arrived on Steep Holm. Though it lacks all the qualities of ordinary Valerian, it does have its uses. Both leaves and roots can be eaten, as a salad or cooked.

Another crevice plant, particularly frequent on the partially-shaded rock faces in the eastern cliffs above the beach, is the Wall Pennywort, or Navelwort (*Umbilicus rupestris*). Each plant is a cluster of small, round leaves, greenish-grey with metallic sheen. Pennywort, its name, must come from the middle ages when the silver penny was England's currency. The fat, fleshy leaves are dimpled at the centre and toothed at the edge. Wall Pennywort is a plant of the western counties, often growing near the sea, but also in profusion on the old stone walls of some south Somerset villages. In Elizabethan London, John Gerard saw it on Westminster Abbey,

The glossy leaves of Wall Pennywort (left), with flower head. A Teasel (right) is visited by a Red Admiral. Butterflies migrate in quantity and hundreds sometimes settle across the island.

growing out of the masonry above a door near Chaucer's tomb. West Country herbalists used its juice in the treatment of epilepsy.

From cliff crevices and scree slopes throughout the island, and even out of the Barracks stonework, grows Pellitory-of-the-wall (*Parietaria diffusa*). It is rich in nitre, and remains one of the best herbal remedies against urinatory malfunction, being taken infused. Gerard also recommended it for coughs, sore throats, toothache, sunburn and piles. This Mediterranean plant may well be another monastic introduction.

Lower down Steep Holm's east cliffs, the first abrupt rock faces are colonised by the Wallflower (*Cheiranthus cheiri*). For the visitor landing in springtime, the sporadic dashes of its strong colour—from yellow through to a deep, rusty red—warm a desolate, grey rock-face. Wallflower can root even on the few stark precipices where the usual Steep Holm vegetation does not find a foothold. The plants are large, old and woody. One clump grows from the iron grate in the first-floor fireplace of the ruined Cliff Cottage. Another colony is truly maritime, occupying a corner of the old Inn walls, immediately above the sea. Steep Holm's Wallflowers all rise from the vertical, and look happier for it than any captive plants in the horizontal plane of a municipal flower bed. The Wallflower is another introduction to Britain from the Mediterranean. The oil contains a digitaline-like glycoside used in perfume, though always diluted, as the scent becomes unpleasant at full strength. Arguably, Wallflowers may have come to Steep Holm with the monks in the 12th century, for monastic gardens were far in advance of the rest.

Scientifically, the vertical wall of cliff surrounding the base of the island has what experts believe is the most remarkable of the island's plants. Buckshorn Plantain (*Plantago coronopus*) grows from cracks and ledges in the rock. It is a botanist's plant, and to the layman not unlike its troublesome lawn-weed relatives. Where the interest lies is that this plant is regarded as a sub-species distinct to Steep Holm and it is the only plant which sports a different form on the island from its mainland types. In the past it was claimed as a separate species and called *Plantago sabrinae* after the Roman name for the Severn estuary. The claim has now been rejected and the plant is regarded as an ecad of *Plantago coronopus*, though it is conceded that it is "a very striking variation of this variable species".

The dry northern slopes have another maritime species, and one which can be included amongst the apothecary plants so typical of Steep Holm. The leaves of the Common Scurvy-grass (*Cochlearia officinalis*) were squeezed for a juice rich in antiscorbutic Vitamin-C. Dietary deficiencies were commonplace in 16th century England and scurvy was the scourge of the great voyages that pushed out Tudor horizons. Scurvy-grass, the predecessor of Nelson's lime-water, was the voyagers' only antidote to a disgustedly debilitating body rot.

Herb Robert (*Geranium robertianum*) is also found on the northern rocks, and it also grows well from the cliff beside the upper section of the path from the beach. It is an opportunist plant that thrives on changes and follows man's disturbance. Herb Robert is quick to root on heaps of stones and brick, while in a completely different setting it is the first plant you find springing from the stump of a sawn-off tree. In size it adapts to conditions and can be anything from a few inches to a straggling two feet. It has red stalks, tiny pink flowers and pointed seed-heads. There was a place for the Herb Robert in folk medicine, though it was probably less used than its name suggests. The Irish gave it to cattle suffering from red-water.

Greater Celandine (*Chelidonium majus*) is a far more interesting plant. It grows beside the rusting railway track on the path through the island's Sycamore wood. The plant is a member of the Poppy family but bears more superficial similarities to a Cranesbill. Snap its stem and the juice—an orange latex—is what Gerard advises as an eye-drop "to sharpen the sight, for it cleanseth and consumeth awaie slimie things that cleave about the ball of the eye and hinder the sight". Wherever it occurs in Britain this plant is an escape from historical cultivation and Mrs Grieve says it is found "nearly always in the neighbourhood of human habitations". Mrs Grieve, published in 1931, adds that Celandine "is a very popular medicine in Russia, where it is said to have proved effective in cases of cancers". It contains the alkaloids chelidonine, chelerythrin (narcotic and poisonous), homochelidonine-A, homochelidonine-B, and also protopine, sanguinarine and chelidoxantain.

Widely distributed across the island there is the ultimate in potent medicine. Hemlock (*Conium maculatum*) was the classical suicide-plant and it is said to have been given to Socrates. Those who did not die of it considered Hemlock was a clean killer as it attacked the body rather than the mind and left the victim to observe his own progressive deterioration. Hemlock is mentioned in Anglo-Saxon medicine as early as the tenth century. Its principal alkaloid, coniine, is still used. In small quantities it is sedative and anti-spasmodic, and was formerly prescribed against rabies. Effects are contrary to those of strychnine. Poisonous doses cause loss of speech, then of breathing, but without impairing mental faculties. Irregular heart beats, convulsions and foaming at the mouth end in total paralysis. It is the green plant that is dangerous; dried, it loses much of its poison. For such deadly poison, the plant looks innocuous. It is about four feet high with light-green parsley-like leaves and a few purple blotches on the stem. From it the mediaeval herbalists produced a sedative.

One herb would have been a useful bonus for the monks as it was on the island already. Rock Samphire (*Crithmum maritimum*), growing from Tower Rock and around the South Landing, is part of the island's native coastal flora. It has long been regarded as the basis of a good pickle.

Stinking Iris (*Iris foetidissima*) is a conspicuous Steep Holm path-plant and grows in clumps beneath the Elder on the slopes between the Barracks and the South Landing. Perhaps it occurs naturally on Steep Holm, but the probability is that it can be added to the catalogue of monastic garden escapes—in which case it is completely right that it should grow amongst the Alexanders in the ruins of the Priory. In Somerset the Stinking Iris was a traditional purgative, "the decoction of the roote" being mixed with a glass of ale. It was a primary medicine for fighting scrofula (tuberculosis of the lymph nodes in the neck with overlying ulceration) which was a much more prevalent disease in past times. To call the plant stinking (let alone *foetidissima*) is a misnomer, as it is no more offensive than others of its family. The West Country name, Roast Beef Plant, is a far more accurate description of the smell from its crushed leaves. Its flowers are less showy than the common garden version, but no less attractive.

Yet another plant of the Elder scrub on the southern cliff has herbal associations. Wood Sage (*Teucrium scorodonia*) was a bitter for beers before hops came into use. It was useful for stimulating urination and applying to wounds and sores. A first-class herb for increasing appetite, it was also once an aid to prompt menstruation. The dosage is one ounce of dried herb infused in one pint of boiling water: a wineglassful three times *per diem*. The leaves are downy and similar to those of the White Dead Nettle, though in flowering the two plants are very different. Wood Sage has stalked spikes of greenish-yellow flowers.

There is a little Hawthorn in this Elder wood on the southern slope, including an old windblown tree 14 feet high and of sizeable girth growing north-west of the winch above the perimeter track. Two shrubs grow at the top of the rock face north of the Barracks. The latter bushes are about eight feet high and investigation of one, in May 1975, showed it was *Crataegus monogyna*, the ordinary species of the English southern hedgerows. This was unexpected as previous 20th century botanical lists for Steep Holm named the less common Midland species of Hawthorn (*C. oxyacanthoides*).

Three other Steep Holm plants qualify for a mention as they are typical of the colours of the western seaboard. Small patches of pink-flowering Thrift (*Armeria maritima*) grow with the grasses on the exposed tip of the island near Rudder Rock and in a sheltered railway cutting on the top of the island. In the lower sections of the southern undercliff, Rock Sea-lavender (*Limonium binervosum*) is equally attractive, with stems of purple flower in late summer. Higher up the cliffs, in the rock crevices, the Yellow Stonecrop (*Sedum acre*) is common. It does best, though, on the south-facing walls of Garden Cottage and Priory Farm where it cascades down the sides of the ruins. The fleshy leaves are obscured in June by a mass of yellow star-shaped flowers. A familiar plant in all limestone country, it can tenaciously grip the roofs and gutters of houses and barns, and it does not need much imagination to visualise the two Steep Holm cottages with Yellow Stonecrop on their pantiles. Confusingly, this plant has a different name in each flower book you open, and it is alternatively called Wall-Pepper or Biting Stonecrop.

This account has concentrated on the plants of Steep Holm which are sufficiently noticeable and accessible to be spotted by visitors. They can be regarded as forming the island's primary vegetation, and in many cases its secondary layer as well. The plants that have been ignored are those which are so hidden or localised that you are unlikely to see them—and often Herring Gull predation for nest building and territory clearances have been carried out on such a scale that their continued existence may be problematical. Many gulls have to keep clear what is literally an airstrip so that they can continue to land at their nests. Plucking of vegetation is also a common displacement activity in disputes and it is impossible to overstate the degree of control which the thousands of gulls exercise over the island's plant life.

Apart from the Nettles, which grow up amongst Alexanders and take over from it by midsummer, only Ground Ivy survives as a surface cover plant. The light-starvation caused by the Alexanders jungle is severe between May and July and blocks any potential competition. The quantity of its seed in the soil all over the island, and its ability to take advantage of climatic changes, ensures that it retains its monopoly.

Annual Mercury (*Mercurialis annua*) takes the place of the Alexanders in October, producing a second crop of lush, light greens across the island, though its place in the cycle was not noticed until 1952.

Of all plants, Nettles (*Urtica dioica* and *U. urens*) are inevitable followers of man, and the great colonisers of disturbed ground. On Steep Holm they share the Alexanders meadow, thrive in the Sycamore wood, grow throughout the Elder scrub, and survive stunted on exposed cliff-faces. Yet these too are almost certainly definite deliberate introductions as in mediaeval times nettle was regarded as amongst the most valuable of all plants.

Its fibre was used as a cheap substitute for flax and linen even as late as the 17th century in Scotland; it was used for coarse domestic cloth, for napkins, bedsheets, tablecloths, etc. and for fishing-net twine. When Germany ran short of cotton in the 1914-18 war, nettle-weaving was resumed. It makes a good spring vegetable: boil the green tops in a minimum of water, like spinach. It is still commonly eaten in the Greek islands and other parts of Southern Europe. The effect is mildly laxative. The roots can also be earthed up and blanched like sea-kale. Nettle Beer is famous as a remedy for gout and rheumatism. It makes a good gargle, and is a powerful checker of bleeding. It was finally, with *Cochlearia*, a very ancient remedy against scurvy. Among its other manifold uses are as a dyeing plant (the leaves give a permanent green, the roots, a yellow) and as a fly-repellent. An old housewive's trick was to hang a bunch of nettle stems in a larder. The nettle in fact is one of the most useful of all plants; and it is an irony that its stinging properties have made it among the most hated by modern man.

While this account has emphasised the quantity of introduced plants, and suggested this is far from accidental, there are other ways in which an island flora can be enriched. Water carriage as a method for seeds arriving on Steep Holm was dismissed, however, by R.C. McLean and H.A. Hyde in the Journal of Botany in 1924. They pointed out that out of nearly a thousand British species which had been tested, only fifteen percent had seeds capable of floating for a week or longer. The island geography, with the curtain of rocks preventing the high tide line washing against ground which could support plant life, is another factor that would lessen the sea dispersal of seeds. Wind is a far more convincing agent. In 1924 figures were drawn up for members of the *Compositae* family, comparing those with downy seeds against those without. In Somerset generally there were 61 such plants with downy seeds, and 23 without. On the island the ratio was 23 to four, showing Steep Holm had a distinctly higher proportion of plants producing seeds which are potentially wind-blown.

The most recent professional assessment of Steep Holm's flora is over 20 years old. It comes from a notable limestone botanist, the late Dr. J.E. Lousley, who spent four hours ashore on 15 May 1954. But there is no need to make allowance either for the age of his report or the short time spent on the island. Lousley's notes are still fresh and stimulating.

His view was that the 1954 flora of the island totalled about 225 species, although it was difficult for him to be precise. The all-time total had reached 261 flowering plants and ferns but that figure was cumulative. It did not allow for deletions. The war years and the increasing dominance of Alexanders in the general vegetation pattern had extinguished many species. Most of the survivors from those that had always been numerically weak were now localised and represented by only a few specimens. "It is evident," Lousley wrote, "that very many of the recorded species must occur in very small quantity."

The total number of species counted was unexceptional, but another factor balanced this apparent lack of numbers, and Lousley stressed: "I was impressed by the uniformity rather than variety in the flora." He counted 84 different species on the island in 1954. That is probably as many as one botanist is going to find on a single trip. Macgregor Skene managed 85 on his visit in 1938.

Amongst the most valuable information to come from the 1954 report is a detailed account of the status of the Peony, which must then have been at its peak. Thirty years before, in 1923, almost all the island Peonies were growing together, in one dense patch of about five square yards "at the very edge of the precipice" with Blackberry bushes "the most dangerous aggressor to the Peony on its precarious perch". In 1943, W.G.M. Jones, serving on the island, remembers seeing about 60 to 80 plants in "a healthy area of growth, maybe 25 to 30 feet square" on the "somewhat damp" cliff facing Weston. By 1954 the plant had achieved its optimum spread across the eastern slopes which rather surprised Lousley. He noted "earlier accounts speak of two patches, whereas now it is scattered about on the cliffs above the landing place, and numerous seedlings were seen. Also it is not now restricted to the top of the cliffs but comes well down." Much of this area he classed as "mainly inaccessible" and the Peony was doing well in the struggle for survival against other plants: "There is little doubt that this was introduced in ancient times but it competes with the native vegetation, sets seed, and maintains itself." There was no need for Lousley to suggest any conservation measures to help the Peony.

Obviously its decline had not yet started. His observations about its ability to compete with the other vegetation show the Peony can withstand apparently adverse conditions, but Lousley does not go into enough detail for this information to be much use in any future protection policy. There are degrees of competition and the area above the beach has been swept with a tangle of Alexanders, Bramble, Ivy and Elder since 1954. All the Peonies were overwhelmed, and it was only to the north of the cliff path, under the shade of Sycamore trees, that occasional plants survived. These are said to have been eliminated by chronic rust disease and apart from one thriving plant on an east-facing ledge, the only healthy specimens are in a tiny square of gardened ground on the top of the island to the west of the Barracks. Seeds from these plants were sent in 1976 to the micro-propagation unit at Kew Gardens. The seeds lie dormant for their first year and germinate in the next. The Kenneth Allsop Trust, at Kew and in John Fowles's Dorset garden and elsewhere, is growing a quantity of young peonies for reintroduction to the island in 1982 and onwards. Sites for these plants are being carefully chosen in sheltered

Opposite: Sycamores have brought standing timber to the eastern cliffs. The wood covers about two acres, and has smothered the island's former Peony ledges. The incline railway was cut in 1941.

but semi-open cliffside positions.

The thinking of J.E. Lousley still underlies the Nature Conservancy's attitude to Steep Holm. The first three conclusions in a 1975 report by the Conservancy's regional staff, into the island's main features, are taken from the Lousley report. He considered the "long succession of visits from naturalists who have made records have provided an historical background which is of great value in interpreting the present flora." The distinguished visitors included W. Turner (before 1562), de l'Obel (1581), J. Newton (about 1688) and Banks and Lightfoot (1773). Next, Lousley and the Conservancy mention the "several rare species of plant growing on the island", by which they mean specifically the Peony, Wild Leek, Caper Spurge, and the Buckshorn Plantain. Thirdly they both draw the attention of conservationists to the meadow of Alexanders, covering several acres across the top of the island, "which is a unique feature".

It was the botanical importance of Steep Holm that led to its being listed as a "Site of Special Scientific Interest" under section 23 of the National Parks and Access to the Countryside Act 1949. This was a notification by the Nature Conservancy to the local planners that the island has exceptional ecological value, giving them a reason for resisting any development applications.

On 16 May 1975 Miss Nettie Bonnar, at the Conservancy's national headquarters in Belgrave Square, made an encouraging statement welcoming the Trust's efforts: "We are of the opinion that, under suitable management it is quite likely that the scientific interest and educational potential of the site could be further developed: if the Trust does acquire the island, therefore, the Nature Conservancy Council would welcome the opportunity to discuss with them how this might best be achieved."

The great need is to monitor the island's species, particularly the changing status of the rarer and more interesting plants. Active conservation steps will have to be taken in the 1980s if the island is not to slide into a botanical decline with a mounting tally of disappearing species. Generally, the island's flora is dominated by the accidents of past introductions and their reversions to the wild. With this background of an artificial, man-made botany, a strong case can be argued for regarding Steep Holm as an overgrown garden. The losers in this power struggle have been the natural, indigenous plants of the limestone rocks. A visit to Brean Down, the closest mainland to Steep Holm, offers a striking ecological contrast.

A worthwhile policy might be to introduce the treasured, and often hard-pressed, natives of the Mendip Hills and Avon Gorge, to whose geology Steep Holm belongs. Obvious contenders are the Cheddar Pink (*Dianthus gratianopolitanus*) from the famous tourist spot, *Veronica spicata* and *Allium sphaerocephalon* from the Bristol area, and the White Rock Rose (*Helianthemum appenninum*) and Bee Orchid (*Ophrys apifera*) both of which grow on Brean Down. They are all rarities with ample beauty to repay the effort of bringing them to Steep Holm. The stock for such an experiment could be found on endangered mainland sites, and the creation of a "plant-bank" of threatened species in an island sanctuary is an opportunity too rare to be dismissed by purist considerations.

To take the idea a stage further, a pen of wide-mesh wire netting in the more varying areas of vegetation near Garden Cottage (the wire to prevent Herring Gull

Jungle of Alexanders, surrounding the Barracks. The correct term for it is 'meadow'
but this can be misleading for a plant that grows more than six feet high during a damp
spring.

plant-plucking) could enable a colony of orchids to be re-established on the island. However, an additional problem is that gull guano has increased the nitrates and phosphates in the soil to a level where much island ground is now unsuitable for its former alkaline-needing limestone plants. Whatever role the island is given, knowledge of its botany needs to be advanced a stage further. For the moment, the fullest listing of Steep Holm plants is that compiled by Professor Macgregor Skene in 1938 and this is printed here with the addition of species noted subsequently (the year they were first recorded being given in brackets). Notes are given on their current status and in some cases extinction from the island flora. It is possible several more should be written off as an island will always lose more species than it gains. Cowslips, for instance, were "very common" when Rev. F.L. Blathwayt visited Steep Holm on 18 April 1907 and were still present on the east side of the island in 1954, but there was none by 1970. It is a loss to the Steep Holm herbal, though paralleled by its decline nationally. Fermented Cowslip flowers made one of the strongest of English country wines, pale yellow and almost of liqueur standard.

Changes would have happened to the vegetation of Steep Holm during this century even if there had been no explosion of Herring Gull numbers, and the consequent saturation with nitrates. Even without the predominance of Nettles, Elder and Alexanders, the island was bound to have its reversion to scrubland from the moment that modern economic conditions put an end to subsistence farming. With this, systematic grazing ceased, and the current contribution made by rabbits and introduced deer is nothing to the cropping that used to take place. Dr Louis Frost, of the Department of Botany at Bristol University, has charted similar changes on the sides of the Avon Gorge, where the sheep ceased to graze in the 1920s. The appearance of the rough grassy slopes, studded with rare flowers in quantity, was one that is portrayed on every print of the area since the middle ages. Since the sheep have gone, however, dense tree growth has smothered the rocks and recreated the primaeval forest conditions of 6,000 years ago. Some of the Gorge's most famous species, like the Honewort which was first recorded there in 1562, can now be found only in localised places where modern human disturbance imitates the conditions that the sheep used to create everywhere. Honewort survives where people have tramped the grass short, and is given its opportunities when children push a few stones over the edge of the precipice. Likewise, on Steep Holm, the disturbed ground beside the paths often gives less usual plants a niche beside the jungle of Nettles, Alexanders and Bramble that they would never otherwise penetrate. This applies to Caper Spurge, Hemlock, Greater Celandine, Mullein and even a single Mediterranean Milk Thistle, yet in the habitats created by human intrusion, they are instantly vulnerable to the feet and swipes of the visitors.

In this Steep Holm plant list, specific names are given first *in italics*, followed by the common English name where the plant has one. The list has two columns appended. The first gives the date of the first record and the second a very rough guide to status, in that 'O' represents occurrence in 1975 to 1977, 'C' shows it to be common in that period and '?' indicates questionable occurrence.

The first point which should be borne in mind refers to the records of 1883. Many finds of that visit have not been recorded since, but conditions have changed over the years and it is not possible to say whether there were mistaken identities. In the words of the 1914 survey compiler "later observers feel the party must have been marvellously successful in obtaining certain flowers which have not come under their notice at the same time of year".

The second point is that numerous discrepancies occur in the records. For example, both *Arctium lappa* and *A. minus* are recorded. In the more recent records, Challenger in 1955 gives only *A. lappa*, whereas Graham in 1963 records only *A. minus*. Recent examination of many plants of the genus have only provided records of the latter species. Confirmation of many of the records is impossible to obtain, and the records can only be detailed as originally published, without comment in most cases.

Nomenclature of the Pteridophyta and Angiospermae is that of Clapham, Tutin and Warburg (2nd. edition, 1962), and that of the Bryophyta is that of E. V. Watson (2nd. edition, 1968), that of the Lichenes is from U. K. Duncan (1970) and that of the Fungi is from the latest B.M.S. checklist.

Polypodiaceae (Fern Family)

Phyllitis scolopendrium (L.) Newm. Hart's-tongue Fern	1883	C
Asplenium adiantum-nigrum L. Black Spleenwort	1883	O
Asplenium trichomanes L. Maidenhair Spleenwort	1883	
Asplenium marinum L. Sea Spleenwort	1773	O
Asplenium ruta-muraria L. Wall Rue	1831	
Ceterach officinarum DC. Rusty-back Fern	1923	
Dryopteris filix-mas (L.) Schott Male Fern	1966	O
Polypodium vulgare agg. Polypody	1831	
Polypodium interjectum Shivas	1969	O

Ranunculaceae (Buttercup family)

Anemone nemorosa L. Wood Anemone	1883	
Clematis vitalba L. Traveller's Joy	1883	
Ranunculus acris L. Meadow Buttercup	1883	O
Ranunculus repens L. Creeping Buttercup	1883	O
Ranunculus bulbosus L. Bulbous Buttercup	1891	O
Ranunculus arvensis L. Corn Buttercup	1965	
Ranunculus sceleratus L. Celery-leaved Crowfoot	1965	
Ranunculus ficaria L. Lesser Celandine	1883	

Paeoniaceae (Peony family)

Paeonia mascula (L.) Mill. Wild Peony	c 1803	O

Papaveraceae (Poppy family)

Papaver dubium L. Long-headed Poppy	1891	O
Chelidonium majus L. Greater Celandine	1965	O

Fumariaceae (Fumitory family)

Fumaria capreolata L. Ramping Fumitory	1890	
Fumaria officinalis L. Common Fumitory	1883	

Cruciferae (Cabbage family)

Brassica oleracea L. Wild Cabbage	1837	?
Brassica napus L. Rape/Swede group	1891	
Brassica rapa ssp. *campestris* (L.) Clapham Bargeman's Cabbage	1883	C
Sinapis arvensis L. Charlock	1883	
Diplotaxis muralis (L.) DC. Wall Rocket	1891	
Diplotaxis tenuifolia (L.) DC. Perennial Wall Rocket	1909	
Raphanus maritimus Sm. Sea Radish	1883	
Cakile maritima Scop. Sea Rocket	1883	
Lepidium campestre (L.) R. Br. Field Pepperwort	1883	
Coronopus squamatus (Forsk.) Aschers. Procumbent Swinecress	1963	O
Coronopus didymus (L.) Sm. Lesser Swinecress	1964	O
Capsella bursa-pastoris (L.) Medic. Shepherd's Purse	1891	O
Cochlearia officinalis L. Common Scurvy-grass	1883	O
Cochlearia danica L. Early Scurvy-grass	c 1688	
Erophila verna (L.) Chevall. Common Whitlow-grass	1890	
Cardamine hirsuta L. Hairy Bittercress	1883	O
Barbarea vulgaris R.Br. Winter Cress	1883	
Cheiranthus cheiri L. Wallflower	1883	C
Sisymbrium officinale (L.) Scop. Hedge Mustard	1883	O
Arabidopsis thaliana (L.) Heynh. Common Wall Cress	1883	

Resedaceae (Mignonette family)

Reseda luteola L. Weld	1923	C

Violaceae (Violet family)

Viola riviniana Rchb. Common Violet	1909	

Viola reichenbachiana Jord. Ex Bor. Pale Wood Violet	1883	
Polygalaceae (Milkwort family)		
Polygala vulgaris L. Common Milkwort	1891	
Hypericaceae (St John's Wort family)		
Hypericum pulchrum L. Slender St John's Wort	1883	
Hypericum montanum L. Mountain St John's Wort	1890	
Caryophyllaceae (Pink family)		
Silene dioica (L.) Clairv. Red Campion	1883	O
Silene alba (Mill.) E.H.L. Krause White Campion	1891	O
Silene vulgaris (Moench) Garcke Bladder Campion	1891	
Silene maritima With. Sea Campion	1883	O
Cerastium holosteoides Fr. Common Mouse-ear	1891	O
Cerastium glomeratum Thuill. Sticky Mouse-ear	1883	
Cerastium atrovirens Bab. Dark-green Mouse-ear	1883	
Cerastium pumilum Curt. Curtis's Mouse-ear	1891	
Cerastium semidecandrum L. Little Mouse-ear	1891	
Stellaria nemorum L. Wood Chickweed	1883	
Stellaria media (L.) Vill. Common Chickweed	1883	O
Stellaria neglecta Weihe Greater Chickweed	1964	
Sagina apetala Ard. Common Pearlwort	1891	
Sagina maritima Don. Sea Pearlwort	1952	O
Sagina procumbens L. Procumbent Pearlwort	1883	O
Arenaria serpyllifolia agg. Thyme-leaved Sandwort	1836	
Spergula arvensis L. Corn Spurrey	1883	
Spergularia marina (L.) Griseb Lesser Sea Spurrey	1977	O
Chenopodiaceae (Goosefoot family)		
Chenopodium album L. Fat Hen	1883	C
Chenopodium rubrum L. Red Goosefoot	1883	O
Beta vulgaris ssp. *maritima* (L.) Thell. Sea Beet	1883	C
Atriplex hastata L. (?ssp. *glabriuscula* Edmondst.) Hastate Orache	1891	C
Atriplex patula L. Common Orache	1883	
Suaeda maritima (L.) Dum. Herbaceous Seablite	1883	
Suaeda fruticosa Forsk. Shrubby Seablite	1581	?
Salsola kali L. Saltwort	1883	
Malvaceae (Mallow family)		
Malva sylvestris L. Common Mallow	1883	O
Lavatera arborea L. Tree Mallow	1773	C
Linaceae (Flax family)		
Linum catharticum L. Purging Flax	1891	
Geraniaceae (Geranium family)		
Geranium dissectum L. Cut-leaved Cranesbill	1883	
Geranium molle L. Dovesfoot Cranesbill	1891	O
Geranium robertianum L. Herb Robert	1883	O
Geranium robertianum ssp. *maritimum* (Bab.) H. G. Baker	1923	O
Erodium maritimum (L.) L'Herit. Sea Storksbill	1773	O
Erodium cicutarium (L.) L'Herit. Common Storksbill	1883	O
Oxalidaceae (Wood-sorrel family)		
Oxalis acetosella L. Wood-sorrel	1883	
Aceraceae (Maple family)		
Acer pseudoplatanus L. Sycamore	1883	C

Papilionaceae (Pea family)
Genista anglica L. Petty Whin	1883	?
Ononis repens L. Restharrow	1883	
Medicago lupulina L. Black Medick	1891	
Trifolium dubium Sibth. Lesser Yellow Trefoil	1891	
Trifolium campestre Schreb. Hop Trefoil	1891	
Trifolium repens L. White Clover	1883	
Trifolium pratense L. Red Clover	1891	
Anthyllis vulneraria L. Kidney Vetch	1891	
Lotus corniculatus L. Birdsfoot-trefoil	1883	
Lotus pedunculatus Cav. Large Birdsfoot-trefoil	1877	
Vicia hirsuta (L.) S. F. Gray Hairy Tare	1883	
Vicia tetrasperma (L.) Schreb. Smooth Tare	1883	
Vicia sepium L. Bush Vetch	1909	
Vicia sativa L. Common Vetch	1883	
Vicia sativa ssp. *angustifolia* (L.) Gaud.	1909	
Vicia lathyroides L. Spring Vetch	1883	
Lathyrus pratensis L. Meadow Vetchling	1883	

Rosaceae (Rose family)
Rubus caesius L. Dewberry	1964	
Rubus ulmifolius Schott Bramble species	1891	C
Potentilla reptans L. Creeping Cinquefoil	1954	
Rosa canina L. Dog Rose species	1955	O
Rosa dumalis Bechst. Dog Rose species	1890	
Rosa rubiginosa L. Sweet Briar	1923	
Prunus spinosa L. Blackthorn	1938	O
Crataegus monogyna Jacq. Hawthorn	1891	O

Crassulaceae (Stonecrop family)
Sedum telephium L. Orpine	1883	
Sedum acre L. Yellow Stonecrop	1877	C
Umbilicus rupestris (Salisb.) Dandy Wall Pennywort	1883	C

Saxifragaceae (Saxifrage family)
Saxifraga tridactylites L. Rue-leaved Saxifrage	1909	O

Grossulariaceae (Currant family)
Ribes uva-crispa L. Gooseberry	1923	O

Onagraceae (Willowherb family)
Epilobium montanum L. Broad-leaved Willow-herb	1976	O

Araliaceae (Ivy family)
Hedera helix L. Ivy	1831	C

Umbelliferae (Carrot family)
Sanicula europaea L. Sanicle	1883	
Anthriscus sylvestris (L.) Hoffm. Cow Parsley	1923	O
Torilis japonica (Houtt.) DC. Upright Hedge-parsley	1883	
Coriandrum sativum L. Coriander	1887	
Smyrnium olusatrum L. Alexanders	c 1562	C
Conium maculatum L. Hemlock	1773	C
Petroselinum crispum (Mill.) Nyman Parsley	1891	
Pimpinella saxifraga L. Burnet Saxifrage	1891	
Crithmum maritimum L. Rock Samphire	1773	O
Aethusa cynapium L. Fool's Parsley	1877	
Foeniculum vulgare Mill. Fennel	1883	
Pastinaca sativa L. Wild Parsnip	1891	

Heracleum sphondylium L. Hogweed	1890	
Euphorbiaceae (Spurge family)		
Mercurialis perennis L. Dog's Mercury	1883	O
Mercurialis annua L. Annual Mercury	1952	C
Euphorbia lathyrus L. Caper Spurge	1773	O
Polygonaceae (Dock family)		
Polygonum aviculare L. Knotgrass	1883	
Polygonum persicaria L. Red Shank	1953	
Rumex acetosella L. Sheep's Sorrel	1883	
Rumex acetosa L. Common Sorrel	1883	O
Rumex crispus L. Curled Dock	1891	O
Rumex obtusifolius L. Broad-leaved Dock	1975	O
Urticaceae (Nettle family)		
Parietaria diffusa Mert. & Koch Pellitory-of-the-Wall	1831	C
Urtica urens L. Small Nettle	1883	C
Urtica dioica L. Stinging Nettle	1891	C
Moraceae (Fig family)		
Ficus carica L. Fig Tree	1964	O
Plumbaginaceae (Sea-lavender family)		
Limonium vulgare Mill. Common Sea-lavender	1773	?
Limonium binervosum (G. E. Sm.) C. E. Salmon Rock Sea-lavender	1883	O
Armeria maritima (Mill.) Willd. Thrift	1883	O
Primulaceae (Primrose family)		
Primula veris L. Cowslip	1883	
Primula vulgaris Huds. Primrose	1883	O
Anagallis arvensis L. Scarlet Pimpernel	1909	C
Anagallis arvensis ssp. *foemina* (Mill.) Schinz & Thell Blue Pimpernel	1883	
Buddlejaceae (Buddleja family)		
Buddleja davidii Franch. Butterfly Bush	1974	O
Oleaceae (Olive family)		
Syringa vulgaris L. Lilac	1909	
Ligustrum vulgare L. Wild Privet	c 1625	C
Gentianaceae (Gentian family)		
Centaurium erythraea Rafn. Common Centaury	1909	
Blackstonia perfoliata (L.) Huds. Yellow-wort	1877	
Boraginaceae (Borage family)		
Cynoglossum officinale L. Hounds-tongue	1877	O
Anchusa arvensis (L.) Bieb. Bugloss	1909	O
Myosotis scorpioides L. Water Forget-me-not	1909	
Myosotis arvensis (L.) Hill Common Forget-me-not	1891	O
Myosotis discolor Pers. Changing Forget-me-not	1909	
Myosotis ramosissima Rochel Early Forget-me-not	1891	
Echium vulgare L. Viper's Bugloss	1909	
Solanaceae (Nightshade family)		
Hyoscyamus niger L. Henbane	1831	C
Solanum dulcamara L. Woody Nightshade	1965	O
Solanum nigrum L. Black Nightshade	1965	O
Solanum tuberosum L. Potato	1963	O
Scrophulariaceae (Figwort family)		

Verbascum thapsus L. Great Mullein	1877	C
Antirrhinum majus L. Snapdragon	1891	
Scrophularia nodosa L. Common Figwort	1891	O
Digitalis purpurea L. Foxglove	1891	
Veronica chamaedrys L. Germander Speedwell	1891	
Veronica serpyllifolia L. Thyme-leaved Speedwell	1883	
Veronica arvensis L. Wall Speedwell	1891	
Veronica persica Poir. Buxbaum's Speedwell	1891	O
Veronica agrestis L. Field Speedwell	1923	
Euphrasia officinalis agg. Eyebright (group of species)	1883	
Odontites verna (Bell.) Dum. Red Bartsia	1883	

Orobanchaceae (Broomrape family)

Orobanche hederae Duby Ivy Broomrape	1946	O

Verbenaceae (Verbena family)

Verbena officinalis L. Vervain	1883	

Labiatae (Mint family)

Thymus drucei Ronn. Thyme	1883	
Calamintha ascendens Jord. Common Calamint	1891	O
Prunella vulgaris L. Self-heal	1938	
Ballota nigra L. BlackHorehound	1883	
Lamium amplexicaule L. Henbit	1890	O
Lamium maculatum L. Spotted Dead-nettle	1883	
Lamium purpureum L. Red Dead-nettle	1975	C
Glechoma hederacea L. Ground Ivy	1883	C
Marrubium vulgare L. White Horehound	1883	
Teucrium chamaedrys L. Wall Germander	1877	
Teucrium scorodonia L. Woodsage	1831	C

Plantaginaceae (Plantain family)

Plantago major L. Greater Plantain	1953	O
Plantago media L. Hoary Plantain	1883	
Plantago lanceolata L. Ribwort Plantain	1883	O
Plantago maritima L. Sea Plantain	1883	
Plantago coronopus L. var. *sabrinae* Card. & Bak. Buckshorn Plantain	c 1845	O

Campanulaceae (Bellflower family)

Campanula latifolia L. Giant Bellflower	1883	
Campanula rotundifolia L. Harebell	1883	

Rubiaceae (Bedstraw family)

Sherardia arvensis L. Field Madder	1891	
Galium cruciata (L.) Scop. Crosswort	1883	
Galium mollugo L. Hedge Bedstraw	1890	
Galium verum L. Lady's Bedstraw	1883	
Galium saxatile L. Heath Bedstraw	1938	
Galium aparine L. Cleavers	1883	O
Rubia peregrina L. Wild Madder	1891	

Caprifoliaceae (Honeysuckle family)

Sambucus nigra L. Elder	1831	C
Symphoricarpos rivularis Suksdorf Snowberry	1909	

Valerianaceae (Valerian family)

Centranthus ruber (L.) DC. Red Valerian	1883	C

Dipsacaceae (Teasel family)

Dipsacus fullonum L. Teasel	1909	C

Compositae (Daisy family)

Helianthus annuus L. Sunflower	1965	O
Senecio jacobaea L. Ragwort	1831	C
Senecio squalidus L. Oxford Ragwort	1962	
Senecio viscosus L. Stinking Groundsel	1883	
Senecio vulgaris L. Groundsel	1883	C
Senecio vulgaris var. *radiatus* Koch Groundsel (rayed form)	1953	O
Tussilago farfara L. Coltsfoot	1883	
Inula conyza DC. Ploughman's Spikenard	1883	
Inula crithmoides L. Golden Samphire	1773	
Filago germanica (L.) L. Cudweed	1883	
Filago minima (Sm.) Pers. Slender Cudweed	1877	
Bellis perennis L. Daisy	1883	O
Chrysanthemum segetum L. Corn Marigold	1883	
Chrysanthemum leucanthemum L. Ox-eye Daisy	1883	O
Carlina vulgaris L. Carline Thistle	1883	
Arctium lappa L. Greater Burdock	1877	
Arctium minus Bernh. Lesser Burdock	1909	C
Carduus tenuiflorus Curt. Slender Thistle	1952	C
Carduus nutans L. Musk Thistle	1877	O
Carduus acanthoides L. Welted Thistle	1883	O
Cirsium vulgare (Savi) Ten. Spear Thistle	1966	O
Cirsium arvense (L.) Scop. Creeping Thistle	1883	O
Cirsium acaulon (L.) Scop. Stemless Thistle	1883	
Silybum marianum (L.) Gaertn. Mediterranean Milk Thistle	1977	
Centaurea scabiosa L. Greater Knapweed	1883	
Centaurea nigra L. Lesser Knapweed	1883	
Lapsana communis L. Nipplewort	1976	O
Hypochaeris radicata L. Common Cat's Ear	1891	O
Leontodon autumnalis L. Autumn Hawkbit	1891	
Leontodon hispidus L. Rough Hawkbit	1891	O
Picris echioides L. Bristly Ox-tongue	1891	O
Sonchus oleraceus L. Smooth Sow-thistle	1891	O
Sonchus asper (L.) Hill Prickly Sow-thistle	1963	O
Hieracium vulgatum auct. angl., ?Fr. Common Hawkweed	1883	
Hieracium pilosella L. Mouse-ear Hawkweed	1891	
Crepis capillaris (L.) Wallr. Smooth Hawksbeard	1938	O
Taraxacum officinale Weber, sensu lato Dandelion	1890	C
Taraxacum laevigatum (Willd.) DC., sensu lato Lesser Dandelion	1890	O

Liliaceae (Lily family)

Endymion non-scriptus (L.) Garcke Bluebell	1883	O
Allium ampeloprasum L. Wild Leek	c 1625	O

Iridaceae (Iris family)

Iris foetidissima L. Stinking Iris	1877	C

Orchidaceae (Orchid family)

Ophrys apifera Huds. Bee Orchid	1877	
Orchis mascula (L.) L. Early Purple Orchid	1883	

Araceae (Arum family)

Arum maculatum L. Cuckoo Pint	1831	C

Cyperaceae (Sedge family)

Carex flacca Schreb. Carnation Grass	1907	

Gramineae (Grass family)
Bromus sterilis L. Barren Brome — 1891
Bromus erectus Huds. Upright Brome — 1883 O
Bromus mollis L. Lop Grass — 1964 O
Bromus thominii Hard. Lop Grass species — 1883
Hordeum murinum L. Wall Barley — 1883 O
Hordeum secalinum Schreb. Meadow Barley — 1883
Festuca ovina L. Sheep's Fescue — 1891 O
Festuca longifolia Thuill. Hard Fescue — 1883
Festuca rubra L. Creeping Fescue — 1883
Festuca rubra ssp.*commutata* Gaud. Chewing's Fescue — 1923
Festuca rubra var.*pruinosa* (Hack.) Howarth Salt-marsh Fescue — 1953
Festuca pratensis Huds. Meadow Fescue — 1883
x *Festulolium loliaceum* (Huds.) P.Fourn. Hybrid Fescue — 1923
Lolium perenne L. Perennial Rye-grass — 1883
Poa annua L. Annual Meadow-grass — 1883
Poa trivialis L. Rough Meadow-grass — 1964
Poa pratensis L. Smooth Meadow-grass — 1883
Poa subcaerulea Sm. Spreading Meadow-grass — 1891 ?
Catapodium rigidum (L.) C.E. Hubb. Fern Grass — 1877
Catapodium marinum (L.) C.E. Hubb. Stiff Sand-grass — 1923
Briza media L. Quaking Grass — 1891
Dactylis glomerata L. Cocksfoot — 1883 O
Dactylis glomerata var.*collina* (Schlechtd.) Cocksfoot variety — 1923
Helictotrichon pubescens (Huds.) Pilger Hairy Oat-grass — 1891
Helictotrichon pratense (L.) Pilger Meadow Oat-grass — 1883
Arrhenatherum elatius (L.) Beauv. ex J. & C. Presl False Oat-grass — 1883
Trisetum flavescens (L.) Beauv. Golden Oat-grass — 1883
Aira caryophyllea L. Silvery Hair-grass — 1883
Anthoxanthum odoratum L. Sweet Vernal-grass — 1883
Phalaris canariensis L. Canary Grass — 1965
Agrostis canina L. (?ssp.*montana* (Hartm.) Hartm.) Brown Bent-grass — 1883
Agrostis stolonifera L. Creeping Bent — 1883

BRYOPHYTA
Musci (Mosses)
Fissidens taxifolius Hedw. — 1966
Fissidens cristatus Wils. — 1954
Tortula intermedia (Brid.) Berk. — 1923
Barbula convoluta Hedw. — 1923
Grimmia pulvinata (Hedw.) Sm. — 1969
Bryum donianum (?) — 1923
Mnium longirostrum Brid. — 1954
Mnium undulatum Hedw. — 1966
Mnium punctatum Hedw. — 1966
Acrocladium cuspidatum (Hedw.) Lindb. — 1923
Scorpiurium circinatum (Brid.) Fleisch. & Loeske — 1923
Camptothecium sericeum (Hedw.) Kindb. — 1923
Camptothecium lutescens (Hedw.) B., S. & G. — 1923
Rhynchostegiella tenella (Dicks.) Limpr. — 1923
Pleurozium schreberi (Brid.) Mitt. — 1923
Hypnum cupressiforme Hedw. — 1966
Hypnum cupressiforme var. *tectorum* B., S. & G. — 1923

Hepaticae (Liverworts)

Steep Holm – a case history

Reboulia hemisphaerica (L.) Raddi	No date [1]
Metzgeria furcata (L.) Dum.	1923
Plagiochila spinulosa (Dicks.) Dum.	1954
Lophocolea bidentata (L.) Dum.	1954
Porella platyphylla (L.) Lindb.	1923
Marchesinia mackaii (Hook) Gray	No date [2]
Frullania tamarisci (L.) Dum.	1923

Algae—Freshwater

Prasiola crispa (Lightf.) Menegh.	1954

Algae—Marine

Cladophora rupestris	1938
Enteromorpha intestinalis	1938
Ulva lactuca	1938
Ascophyllum nodosum	1966
Fucus ceranoides	1966
Fucus serratus	1938
Fucus spiralis	1966
Fucus vesiculosus	1938
Pelvetia caniculata	1938
(Ceramium sp.	1966
(Hildenbrandia sp.	1966
(Lithophyllum sp.	1966
(Rhodochorton sp.	1966

Lichenes (Lichens)

Verrucaria muralis Ach.	1923
Verrucaria hochstetteri Fr.	1923
Protoblastenia rupestris (Scop.) Steiner var. *calva* (Dicks.) Steiner	1923
Toninia medoidea (Nyl.) Zahlbr.	1923
Bacidia muscorum (Ach.) Mudd.	1923
Cladonia furcata (Huds.) Schrad.	1923
Cladonia rangiformis Hoffm.	1923
Cladonia pyxidata (L.) Hoffm.	1923
Cladonia pocillum (Ach.) O. J. Rich	1923
Lecanora dispersa (Pers.) Sommerf.	1923
Lecanora helicopis (Wahlenb. ex Ach.) Ach.	1923
Lecania erysibe (Ach.) Mudd.	1923
Physcia pulverulenta (Schreb.) Hampe	1923
Physcia tenella (Scop.) DC em Bitt.	1923
Caloplaca holocarpa (Hoffm.) Wade.	1923
Caloplaca ferruginea (Huds.) Th. Fr.	1923
Caloplaca citrina (Hoffm.) Th. Fr.	1923
Caloplaca ochracea (Schaer.) Flag.	1923
Caloplaca aurantia (Pers.) Hellb.	1923
Caloplaca heppiana (MullArg.) Zahlbr.	1923
Xanthoria parietina (L.) Th. Fr.	1923
Placynthium nigrum (Huds.) Gray	1923

---

[1] Undated record by W. Watson in his 'Liverworts of Somerset', written in the copy presented to Bristol Museum. Also recorded 1954.

[2] Similarly undated record by Watson, op.cit.

Fungi

Agaricales
Clitocybe flaccida (Sow. ex Fr.) Kummer	1976
Lepiota procera (Scop. ex Fr.) S. F. Gray	1976
Marasmius androsaceus (L. ex Fr.) Fr.	1976
Marasmius oreades (Bolt ex Fr.) Fr.	1976
Mycena vitilis (Fr.) Quel.	1976
Stropharia coronilla (Bull ex Fr.) Quel.	1976

Gasteromycetales
Langermannia gigantea (Batsch ex Pers.) Rostk.	1976

Heterobasidiomycetes
Hirneola auricula-judae (Bull) Fr.) Schroet	1976

Ascomycetes
Peziza varia (Hedwig) Fr.	1976
Nectria cinnabarina (Tode ex Fr.) Fr.	1976

Uredinaceae
Puccinia smyrnii Corda.	1877

Crofting ruins

Rodney Legg

THE DARK AGES of Steep Holm history stretch from the time of the monks to 1776. In that year a "tenement" was built for fishermen stranded on the island by storms. Shipwrecks happen each year along this difficult coast, but Steep Holm only figures in two cases, and both are in historically recent times. *Rebecca*, a West India Company merchantman, was wrecked on the island in 1810, and the Spanish barque *Anita* went down with all her crew in 1901.

The "tenement" is believed to be the cottage ruin in dense undergrowth to the west of the Priory foundations, from where much of its stone must have been robbed. It is about 33 feet long by 15 feet wide with chimneys either end and a door in the south side. There were windows in each wall except the west where there was a large fireplace with a corbelled alcove. Upstairs, was a loft. Outside there was a lean-to extension on the west end and a privy beyond. Because of its position next to the mediaeval ruins, the cottage is called Priory Farm, and seems to be the building where Thomas Clark, one of the island's botanical visitors, had tea in 1831: "The old house on the top of the island, and near the eastern end, has been in part repaired for the accommodation of the workmen. Here we dined off the sandwiches and tarts with which we were provided, in a room which reminded us of banditti. It contained three or four small beds, and the pots, frying pans, and other cooking apparatus of the whole inhabitants of the island. We however were as little disposed to be dissatisfied with our dining-room as with our dinner, and I know not whether we the more enjoyed this repast or our far more elegant tea-supper when we got back to our hotel at Weston."

Further west from Priory Farm is another single-storey ruin, called Garden Cottage, which stands at the north edge of a large stone-walled enclosure and is also of indeterminate age. From the bricks in its floors, and ridge-tiles stamped "Phillips

Opposite: Cliff Cottage was demolished by the Royal Engineers in 1941, the builders of the railway. The left wall is the living rock-face.

and Son, Weston-super-Mare", the date would appear to be mid-19th century. Now, like the other farmstead, it is roofless with walls standing about eight feet high, though a gable end is at full height. There is a piece of carved 1867 masonry, from one of the gun batteries, lying amongst rubble in the north wall. The croft-like appearance of the building shows its origins, as it has the design which archae-ologists describe as a long-house; an extended building with the people living one end and the animals at the other. The evidence of the tiles places its roofing, at least, to a dateable period. Charles Phillips established a pottery on the north side of Locking Road at Weston in 1847, calling himself the Royal Potteries in 1856, and selling the business to John Matthews in 1871. Originally, Garden Cottage may have had a thatched roof, as its pitch seems to have been steepened to take the tiles.

Harrison Matthews, carrying out a survey of the island in 1938, found "some of the grates and a small kitchen stove still in place, as are the wooden door and window jambs. Roofing felt, too, still covers the collapsed roof of a small shed. At one side of the house there is a cemented tank, which is still watertight and filled with rainwater. The enclosure was evidently cultivated as a garden, and lines of stones still show the boundaries of the garden beds. This is not, however, the old garden of the Priory, which is said now to be covered by the Garden Battery. Both the enclosure and the building appear to have been made since the fortifi-cations were constructed in 1867." The enclosure at Garden Cottage covers nearly an acre, its north and west boundaries marked by stone walls and elder trees, the other two sides being engulfed by impenetrable privet scrub.

The other part of the island with ruins is the area beside and above the beach. Architecturally, Cliff Cottage is the island's most adventurous building; it is a rect-angle with its entire north wall being the cliff-face, rendered with plaster over the living rock. There is one large recess in this wall, having an arched top, and a similar arch above a door. It was the most recently intact of the Steep Holm ruins, still having a sound roof in the 1930s. It had been used as a store for fishing gear up to the winter of 1931, the year when the iron stakes across the shingle spit last carried nets. Cliff Cottage was pulled apart by the army in 1941 as its south-east corner stood directly in the way of an incline railway which was being cut in a series of precise sections along the course of a trackway that had previously meandered to the top of the island.

In all the older accounts of Steep Holm, the cottage on the cliffs is not regarded as having any real antiquity. It is described alternatively as a cottage for the staff at the inn or a fisherman's shelter. Both statements are probably true, but the build-ing looks far too well built to have originated in a supplementary fashion, and there is one other clue that has been ignored—its position. Cliff Cottage stands on the first ramp of level ground above the beach, and it is the beach rather than the Victorian-made South Landing which must be regarded as Steep Holm's age-old landing place. Even today, despite the legacy of the South Landing jetty, Steep Holm's regular boatman, John Watts, usually prefers to drop and collect people from the beach. On exceptionally calm days he can even ram the *mv Jane* into the shingle and snatch half an hour ashore before she is lifted by the tide. The *Jane*

Opposite: Arched doorway at Cliff Cottage. Another, on the other side of the fireplace, is blocked with rubble. Above is the upstairs grate.

is a valid indicator of past times as she is a traditional open craft, with an engine as the sole innovation. Despite looking unprotected, she has a remarkable stability and Sir Peter Scott came back from an expedition to Steep Holm saying she was capable of crossing the Atlantic. Boatmen today are not going to tackle Steep Holm much differently from the way their predecessors have for centuries.

In short, the shingle beach is the only historic landing-place for Steep Holm. But the physical shape of the island makes another point equally clear. Because of the abruptly tilting strata which rise vertically behind the beach, the only exit is in the north-east corner, and that climbs above the rocks to the front wall of Cliff Cottage. That is why the site of Cliff Cottage is significant. It stands at the point where visitors to the island at all periods have made their first foothold. As those who live on islands are dependent on their boats, it is logical to build where you can watch the landing place, and this piece of ground may have a history longer than the Priory.

The cottage is only 50 yards from Steep Holm's mediaeval well, and stands beside the only path approaching it from the rest of the island. No similar claims for a desirable building plot can be made for any other part of the island. Yet despite its suitability for early occupation, there is little doubt that the present Cliff Cottage is contemporary with the inn and dates from 1832. Neither building is mentioned in Thomas Clark's diary account of his visit to Steep Holm in 1831, though he gives useful information about improvements being carried out to the cliff path, which had led to the discovery of a shell midden: "Several men were employed in cutting a winding road from the little pebble beach, our landing place, at the eastern end of the island, to the top; in part through solid rock; and in one place they had dug through a bed of shells of the common limpet, mixed only with a little loose earth. It was a query how they came there, and at what remote time. Perhaps, numerous as they are, they are only the accumulated heap thrown from time to time from some cottage or hut, of whose inhabitants this shell fish formed, it may be, the principal food; and though we did not observe any vestige of a building very near, the well of good spring water, the only well on the island, is almost close by."

The island had changed hands shortly before Clark's visit, apparently for £700, and the workmen were on the island as the new owner was "about to construct a pier for fishing boats, which will probably be a profitable speculation, for £500 worth of sprats are said to have been caught round the island last season". Their pier was built and lasted till 1860, and it must have been in this period that both Cliff Cottage and the inn were constructed. Out in the rocks, parallel with the inn walls, there is an L-shaped line of stones which were the foundations of a small harbour. L. Harrison Matthews records it in his 1938 report on the island: "On the beach below the inn can be traced the remains of an artificial harbour, which dried out at low tide. It lies in a natural angle of the rocks which formed two sides of it, and the quay walls had been built out on the east and north sides, the entrance being at the north-east corner. The walls are now entirely demolished, but the line of the foundations can still be traced, and the stump of a wooden pile which stood at one side of the entrance, evidently as a fender, is still in position. The foundations are made of large blocks of stone from the beach. This boat harbour, which would have accommodated small ships up to about 30 or 40 tons, judging by the width of the entrance, is apparently contemporary with the inn, and must have been demolished by the sea not long after its construction."

"Discovering" an island like Steep Holm well suited an institutionalised concept

Eastwards from the inn, at low tide, emerges a shingle spit. It used to be staked with a line of nets, the fish being caught as the tide ebbed.

that grew up in Victorian middle class society. Local learned societies were formed all over the country, and their outdoor excursions were a main attraction. A party from Cardiff Naturalists' Society visited Steep Holm in 1877 and stayed overnight at the inn. The inn now comes into the category of a picturesque ruin though that perhaps is a matter of opinion as in 1975 a scout-leader had to be dissuaded from pushing one of its remaining walls into the sea. Until the ravages of the army in 1941 the building still had three storeys, though it was open to the sky, and soon after it was built it had been extended to the north. The building rose out of all proportion to the scale of habitation Steep Holm could support and was a rich man's island residence. The gentleman was Colonel Tynte of Halswell at Bridgwater, but he soon tired of the house and leased the island. The building then became an inn, and had a successful three decades, based on the dubious claim that as Steep Holm was not administratively a part of any parish, no licence was needed. The impossibility of supervision favoured excise evasion and trade was helped by "captive" custom on the island, once the war works started in 1867. Census returns do not show any population on the island from 1801 (when records began) to 1861, but there are then five to nine inhabitants on the island from the 1871 census to 1901, mostly gunners manning the batteries. During this time, in 1884, the claim for excise exemption was challenged and the High Court held that the inn had to be licensed. It had a landlady in 1883, and presumably at the time of the court case, but it was abandoned shortly afterwards. The edge of a beach was a hazardous place to put a house and it was pounded by the sea. Its ground floor could not be used for living quarters and served only to keep the two upper storeys above the level of the storm tides. Upstairs, the floors of the six bedrooms were quick to collapse, and by 1902 the building was ruinous.

Farming and fishing were done on Steep Holm from 1900 till about 1925, though an old brown goat stayed on and was still alive in 1933. Harrison Matthews says that bag-shaped nets were hung from a long row of stakes across the shingle spit: "The ebbing tide swept the fish into the nets which were emptied by the fishermen at low water." In this period, the Barracks was occupied, as it was now the sturdiest building on the island, and the military had no use for it from 1903 to 1941. The two fortified phases provide most of the island's visible history—1941-45 being the last occasion Steep Holm was permanently occupied—and the military archaeology is as exceptional as the island's ecology.

Officialdom, apart from times of national emergency, has ignored the island. In history, Steep Holm enters one charter and then only to mark a boundary. In 1373, when Edward III granted Bristol the status of a county, its western seaward boundary was a line drawn between the islands of Flat Holm and Steep Holm. A boundary stone was set at the top of the beach at the east end of the island and has been replaced several times, the latest block of green sandstone being covered by the stonework that holds the island's beach ladder in place. When mapmakers had to fix a precise position they found they had no knowledge of the location of the stone (before its present obliteration it was often covered by pebbles) and for cartographical convenience set it midway along the northern shore of the island. That is where it is drawn by the Ordnance Survey on the latest official administrative map of Avon county.

This use of the island to fix the limits of Bristol's port does not mean that any part of Steep Holm above the high-tide mark has ever had any legal connections with the city. The island was always a detached piece of Somerset, though never part of a parish, and since April 1974 it has been a detached piece of the new county of Avon. In local government it comes under Woodspring district council and for Parliamentary purposes the island is included in the Weston-super-Mare county constituency. Despite the changes of the 1970s, the island still remains outside any parish, and it is worth repeating this fact as a number of accounts and documents erroneously put it into one mainland parish or another. The mistake even applies to Steep Holm's own title-deed.

Opposite: Strewn rocks from the ruined walls of the inn's tiny harbour. The squared stone in the foreground is one of the facing blocks from an 1868 gun battery.

A 19th century visitor

John Skinner

WESTON, JULY 26 1832: I rose soon after six, and walked with my daughter to the Bath before breakfast; also engaged a boat for sailing, the wind being more favourable, and Joseph I knew would enjoy another trip. We were obliged to walk to Burnback in order to get into a small boat to convey us to a larger which we had hired to take us to the Steep and Flat Holmes.

As it blew briskly, we were not long in reaching the former Island, about seven miles distant from the Bay; while on our course thither I made three sketches, one of the South East side of the Steep Holmes; another of the Flat Holmes, with its Lighthouse, and the Welch Promontory called Pennarth Point beyond: the third was taken as we approached the landing place, of the Steep Holmes, which shows a house now building for an Inn, by Mr. Baker, the Proprietor of the Island which he lately purchased for £700, a very cheap bargain, if it be true that he lets the fishery for £40 a year.

Owing to the carelessness of the man at the helm, we ran on a shingly bank outside the little Harbour, and were obliged to go on shore in the small boat: had it blown hard, the sailing boat we quitted would have been in great danger, as the surf sometimes breaks from 15 to 20 feet high over the bank as we learnt afterwards.

The man says it never occurred to him before to ground on approaching the Island, as he knows every inch of the shore having been occupied in fishing on it from his youth up. In order to render the little Harbour more secure, a number of men are now actually engaged in building a Pier under the new Inn, which will then be frequented perhaps by the coasters coming up the Channel.

There are two small huts on the rock, besides this more extensive habitation,

Opposite: The eastern approaches to Steep Holm, sketched by Rev John Skinner from his boat in 1831. It dates from his second day's excursion and is captioned: "Nearer approach to the Steep Holmes, not having been able to gain the Flat Holmes as we intended." Courtesy British Library, Crown copyright reserved.

both appear to have been recently erected.

In times past, Gildas the Monk, denominated Badonicus, from having been born at Bath, fixed his solitary residence on this rock where he might have realized the miseries he complains of inflicted by the Saxons on the Britons; but being disturbed in his meditations by the Pirates who sailed to and fro, he removed to Glastonbury. The Danes we find also frequently visited this barren rock, and probably made it a receptacle for their plunder taken on the Welch and English shores, and it was the scene of the sad catastrophe which befel them during the reign of Edward, as we learn from the Saxon Chronicle.

As we ascended by a zig zag footpath to the summit, I picked us some fragments of the grey Roman pottery, and noticed also various specimens of coarser ware some laquered over: the earth here looked very dark abounding in limpet shells and the bones of animals, showing that it had been a permanent, not a precarious abode as far back perhaps as the time of the Romans.

An old man—who inhabits the hut at the summit of the rock, and had resided here seven months for the purpose of clearing away the Privet, and wild carrot (Alexanders) which now almost wholly occupy the surface, and planting the soil thus recovered with potatoes and garden stuff—informed me that while digging within the small inclosure which he calls his garden, he came to a vault or cist, seven feet long by four wide; the walls formed of stone without cement, and covered with flat paving stones as he called them: within was a human skull, and skeleton with the skulls of sheep, and other bones, some of which appeared to have been burnt, but there was no appearance of any weapon or vessel.

On my pointing out similar fragments of pottery to those I had before noticed, which were more abundant in his garden, than in the bank I at first examined. He said that he was surprised at the quantities he turned up when digging, and added the people must have been very careless of their ware to break so many pots and pans.

I noticed tiles and bricks some of the former hollowed out after the Roman manner; but they might also be attributable to a later period; perhaps they belonged to the small religious house, said to have been established here by one of the Berkeley family which might have occupied the site of the present Cottage.

I perceived the old man has some cucumbers and cauliflowers in his garden, but complains of the trouble of watering them, as there is only one spring on the Island, and that a small one near the base of the rock, but poor Joseph who felt himself thirsty was very grateful for a supply from the small stream.   Indeed I endeavoured to dissuade him from climbing the Steep, but he seemed so bent on doing it, that he was not to be deterred either by the heat of the weather, or his own short breathing from accomplishing his object, I made a sketch before we ascended the rock of the little Harbour beneath, and a second from the summit, covered by dwarf privet, and quantities of wild Carrot which they here call, I know not for what reason Alexander: the stalk grows to the height of two or three feet, and bears abundance

Opposite: Closer view of the newly-built inn on the eastern side of Steep Holm drawn by John Skinner in 1831. Behind the inn stands the Cliff Cottage, and a path can be seen leading to the top. On the summit is a lookout. Skinner's caption: "A house building as an inn near the landing place." Courtesy British Library, Crown copyright reserved.

of seed, the roots of some being nearly the size of my wrist, for want of better fuel I perceived they bind the stalks of this herb into bundles to burn.

I noticed as I proceeded, where the Privet did not entirely cover the soil, patches of wild Strawberries still bearing fruit, also a plant resembling sage; and in places where there is no depth of earth, a fine herbage covers the rock, supplying food for the rabbits which once abounded here, as well as on the Flat Holmes, but they are now nearly destroyed, since a dog and cat have been admitted as residents by the old man, for he was the Selkirk of the domain till masons were sent over from Weston to build the Inn and the Pier below his elevated habitation.

While persuing the track of a narrow footpath to the northern extremity of the rock worn through the dwarf Privet, by the feet of Pilots, who land here to have a good look out on the Channel, I put up a Thrush, a Sark, and a Wheatear; numbers of screaming, or rather laughing Gulls, soared above my head, apparently inquiring my business there, and the waves murmured against the crags beneath.

During a storm this must be a sublime situation, but I was perfectly satisfied to find it as it was. There seems to have been a wall of loose stones running North and South along the dorsum of the rock from the old man's residence towards the centre where it branches off to the right. I also traced some cross walls.

If the Danes were compelled to sojourn here for any time, they needed some such shelter; if they stowed their plunder here, there was another inducement; or perhaps their officers employed them thus to keep them from murmuring at their privations they were obliged to undergo when the Saxons blockaded the coast.

At the very extreme point northwards nearly opposite to the Flat Holmes and Pennarth Point on the Welch Coast, I noted an oval outpost or signal station, which I should certainly call a Danish work, having before seen similar remains attributable to this people; it measures within the oval about 20 paces by 18; the walls formed of loose stones might have been about four feet wide, the uprights being fixed in the soil, or rather the rock, and the inner space filled up very similar to the workmanship of the vitrified Forts in Scotland, extending along the heights from Inverness almost to the Frith of Clyde.

Dun Iaarl which I particularly examined, is not much larger than this, being situate on the very apex of a pyramidical hill, well adapted to convey signals by fire. Craig Phadric, nearer to Inverness, is of the same oval form, but nearly as large again as the former. Not far from Danes Hill on Mendip, there is a similar Oval Beacon inclosure which I have sketched.

As the Danish Pirates so much frequented the Severn, it would be hardly possible for them to have navigated its dangerous Channel without some such directing Beacons. There might have been a similar one on the Flat Holmes where there is now a Lighthouse, and thus the passage, nearly three miles across, would have been marked out and defended for their nightly descents on the east side of the coast. The name *Holm* is evidently a Danish term, signifying an Island; vide Stockholm; and the family I married into were I presume Islanders, or de Holmes originally. Those of the Isle of Wight evidently were, if they trace so old a pedigree,

Opposite: View of the north-east corner of Steep Holm, from a sketch by John Skinner: "Boat lying at anchor under the Steep Holmes, the coast beyond Weston in the background." Courtesy British Library, Crown copyright reserved.

as do the Oglanders who were established there before the Norman Conquest.

The sketches I took will best describe the situation of the Beacon and the form of the Island, which is said to be nearly a mile and a half in circuit, nearly of an oval shape resembling a Danish Tumulus, described by Old Wormices as a ship turned bottom upwards. When the Privet is grubbed up and the loose stones removed, it is not improbable but weapons or some indicia of its warlike occupiers may be discovered; as Mr Baker the proprietor of the Holm is I find fond of antiquities he will, I dare say, keep a good look out.

Having finished my observations on the summit, I descended with my son and daughter to the beach, where we witnessed the blasting of the rock above the Pier, with an explosion as loud as a Cannon, but we had no apprehension of the falling fragments, being sheltered by a ridge of projecting rock. While waiting for the boat, I made a sketch of this rock, running in horizontal strata, and apparently containing iron ore.

Brean Down and the Brent Knoll are conspicuous objects on the opposite shore. As we sailed away, I sketched the southern end of the Holm, shewing the Pier now building, the New Inn, and a hut occupied by the workmen close to the zig zag path of ascent, with that belonging to the old soldier employed to cultivate the soil.

It blew quite brisk as we returned; we steered to Brean Down, where a fishing boat was trolling, and had caught 34 pairs of Soles, some of which I wished to purchase to send to my mother, but they asked more than she would have got them for at Bath.

I made two sketches of Brean Down whose name indicates the projection above the line of passage which as I have before observed was fortified by the Belgic British before the Romans established themselves in these parts, and inclosed a fort near the centre of the Peninsula to guard the mouth of the river, or rather the estuary, as it was in those days, running up as far as Glastonbury. Roman pottery and coins have been found here, and as some of the grassland is about to be turned up by the plough further remains may be brought to light.

Brean Down forms one arm of West Bay, as Worle Hill does the other, and in the course of years I doubt not the whole of the flat will be gained from the Sea, as was the level ground gained in past times from the Astuary Uxella. I paid the boatman for himself and assistant and boat, half a guinea, and hired them for the following day to take up to the Flat Holmes after breakfast. Owen and his friend Stewart joined us at dinner, they had taken Wells and Cheddar in their way from Camerton to Weston, the little lecture I had previously given respecting our want of accommodation had a good effect, since they were promised comfortable beds, and in the evening perambulated the place, which was quite new to Owen's friend though not to himself. Joseph was not the worse for his exertions.

Opposite: Skinner's strangest contribution to the history of the island is a drawing of an appendage on the northern clifftop that does not exist today, nor is recorded by anyone else: "Site of a signal beacon or a tumulus, but more probably of the former, at the northern extremity of the island facing the coast of Wales." The sketch clearly shows Flat Holm and Pennarth Point in the distance. Courtesy British Library, Crown copyright reserved.

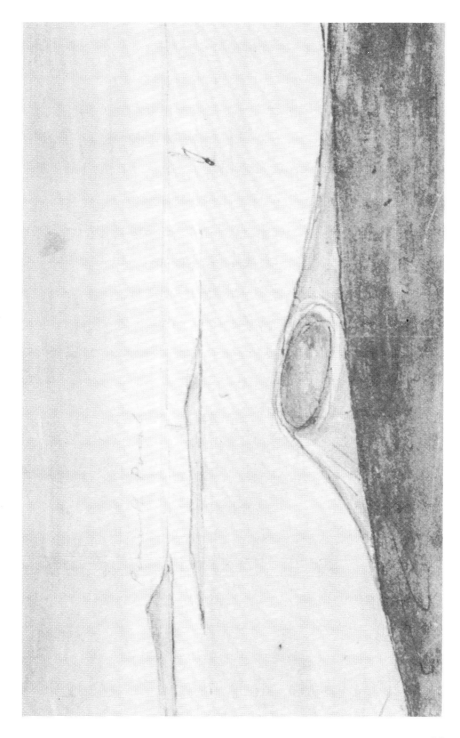

Steep Holm – a case history

JULY 27: I walked with Anna before breakfast to the Bath: afterwards we entered the sailing boat which lay off at anchor head, purposing to reach the Flat Holmes, but the wind dying away, and the tide running strong down Channel, we failed in our purpose, and brought up in a little harbour at the Steep Holmes which we had visited yesterday, but which was quite new to our guests. I took three sketches in Weston Bay; a fourth of the South East side of the Steep Holmes, shewing what is called the Rudder Rock at the northern extremity.

On landing, I pursued my former path to the Fort or Signal station taking en passant another sketch of the Flat Holmes with its Lighthouse just opposite to the summit of the Island, between two upright rocks forming a natural doorway; and beyond that another memorandum of the Danish Signal post with the path leading to it.

We returned to the boat before the tide flowed up Channel with the expectation of reaching the Flat Holmes, but the boatman pretended he could not as the wind then blew, but I was sailor enough to be assured he was purposely imposing on us wishing to hasten our return to Weston that he might get another party on board in the evening, although I had hired the boat for the whole day. I expostulated but to no purpose.

Going round the west side of the Steep Holmes, I made four sketches, and on our return to Weston, two of the Bay. The boatman pretended to press us to go back to the Flat Holmes saying the wind would then enable him to reach it, and was fair for coming back, but he had heard us say that we had ordered dinner at four and meant to walk in the evening.

Before I paid him I took an opportunity to say I should not hire his boat again when I came to Weston, and that he ought to remember the old saying, grasp all lose all.

I walked in the evening with Anna, Owen, and Mrs. Stewart along the sands to Uphill, and returned so completely tired, I was not sorry to go to bed as soon as I penned in my sketches. Joseph evidently is the better for the air and amusement he has found at Weston, but we all agree it is a wretched place to continue in for any length of time.

These extracts and plates from John Skinner's manuscript are reproduced by permission of the British Library Board, reference Add. MS 33728, ff. 39, 50, 38, 44, 45 (drawings 32, 40, 38, 35, 36).

Opposite: Detail of the feature shown in the previous plate. Skinner gives this description: "View of the signal beacon on a larger scale—being about 18 or 20 paces in diameter. It might have been the base of a tumulus as there are several of this diameter but I should rather think it was a Beacon Barrow." The general curve of the cliffedge is suggestive of Tombstone Battery, and the upheaval caused by the Victorian fortifications to this part of the island would account for the disappearance of Skinner's earthwork. Courtesy British Library, Crown copyright reserved.

Farming towards ecology

Rodney Legg

STEEP HOLM, in 1831, came into the hands of the Whartons, an old North of England family. The new owner, Col. Charles Kemeys Kemeys-Tynte of Halswell near Bridgwater, built a house in 1832 above the landing beach, and this building later became the inn. Not that Kemeys-Tynte can be regarded as opting out from ordinary society, for he was provincial grand master of the Somerset lodge of Freemasons for approaching half a century, from May 1820 until his death in November 1860.

Little is known of the use of the island under earlier owners. The closest previous reference to Steep Holm is a 1786 deed showing the island as part of a large Somerset holding owned by John Freke Willes of Northamptonshire. The "messuage on tenement . . . now standing" on the island was in the occupation of Thomas Yateman, though he could have been an absentee tenant. Col. Tynte may not have bought Steep Holm at all but received it through a family settlement. Rumour was that he paid "£7000 or £700" for the island (the former figure is absurd); alternatively that he won it in gambling.

A suggestion that the 1830s development of Steep Holm into a fishing village was not the work of Kemeys-Tynte at all, but carried out by entrepreneur John Baker, was made in 1977 by Stan Rendell of the Banwell Archaeological Society. Baker was a second generation solicitor, his father Samuel being responsible for Weston's Inclosure Act of 1810. The Bakers lived near Blagdon at Batcombe. Rendell's information came from family sources, and whoever is eventually proved to have been responsible for the squandering of so much cash and effort on Steep Holm in the 1830s, it is certain that by the early 1840s the island had been absorbed into the Halswell estate of Kemeys-Tynte.

The possibility that it came to the Tyntes, who held the Wharton baronial title, via another line of the family is at least equally plausible. Briefly, the family history is that Thomas Wharton supported Henry VIII against the Scots and his reward was to become the first Baron Wharton. Philip, the fourth baron, was among the Royalists routed by the Parliamentary army at Edgehill in 1642. Thomas, his son, was author of the doggerel ballad *Lilli Burlero*, ridiculing Irish catholics. Its tune is used to this day as the principal Ulster protestant marching song and, incidentally, as the call-sign for the BBC's world service.

While the Tyntes maintained a direct interest in the island in the 1830s, this did not last. There was soon a succession of tenants. By 1865, Col. Tynte was dead and Dame Anne Cooper, signing on behalf of his estate, granted Her Majesty's Principal Secretary of State for the War Department the use of "parts or parcels" of Steep Holm "for the purpose of constructing batteries, fortifications, and other military works of public defence". Whitehall was thinking in the long-term and took a lease for 999 years, at the annual rent of thirty shillings for each acre the military used. The estate interest was protected to the extent that roadworks on the island were not to be "legally repairable as public roads or highways"; to prevent private rights from being lost. The island was still tenanted.

Her Majestys Principal Secretary of State for the War Department shall have the enjoy the licence or privilege of cutting & quarrying Building Stone from any other part of the sd Island not included in the sd demise for the purpose of constructing the sd public defences Bldgs pier & Landing place on payment of a rent or Royalty of 6 for every Ton that shall be so cut or quarried & 1 for way leave for every Ton of Stone that shall be drawn over the Lands of the sd Devises not included in the sd demise & a rent of £1.10.0 for every acre of surface of the said Lands which shall be used or occupied in such cutting & quarrying of Building Stone or for any purposes connected therewith & on compensating the tenants or occupiers for any damage sustained by them respy thereby —

Extract from the agreement of 10 October 1865 between Dame Anne Cooper and the Secretary of State for War, permitting the military occupation of Steep Holm.

A moment of madness became a triumph in the 1870s. On a cold day in September 1875, 26-year-old Henry Garrett arrived at the South Landing, Steep Holm, after swimming from Weston. Allowing for tidal drift, he managed an estimated seven miles. The island's master gunner fired a shotgun to greet his arrival, and Garrett was then bundled into a rowing boat, to be taken to the inn for sandwiches and coffee.

Throughout the 1870s, before they departed for Flat Holm, the family of Frederick Harris farmed Steep Holm and kept its inn. In fact, the Harris family were at the inn from 1846 to 1885, with the sudden loss of daughter Caroline who eloped to marry Abraham Hurman in Bristol register office on 14 January 1854. They lost their pier in a gale about 1860. The last blow to the Harris's reign was at Axbridge bench on 25 August 1884 when the mainland status quo finally caught up with them. Magistrates decided that the island was not part of Somerset, and licensing laws therefore did not apply. This was so obviously naive that it could never survive an appeal, and this the Inlai Revenue demanded. Bureaucracy eventually won, and the Harris family left. In the summer of 1885 Caroline Davies and her sons Harold and Wallis came, and in a year of what must have been titanic effort, made the island more than just agriculturally self-sufficient. They grew garden produce and vegetables of all kinds, as well as oats and barley, and mowed the uncropped parts of the top of the island for hay to keep their livestock. The animals included three heifers, one steer, five goats, ten pigs, poultry and a donkey. They had a pilot cutter, the *Lance*, which was kept moored off the island, as well as four flat-bottomed fishing boats which were raised up a rock slipway, upon which the beach wall was constructed in 1940. *Spray*, a Weston yacht, came across weekly with stores for the island's eight-man military garrison and the inn. The island had a regular winter fishing industry, employing up to eight men. Nets strung across the shingle caught principally sprats and whiting. Hook lines were set for conger, skate and cod. Catches sometimes reached three tons per tide, and the

Above: The beach before the army arrived. This shot from the mid-1930s shows the inn still three storeys high, and Cliff Cottage (above, right) intact. Photo: J.K. Neale.
Opposite: The inn (right) dates from the frenzied development of the island by the Kemeys-Tynte family in the 1830s. Between it and the beach is a length of 1941 sea walling. Outwards from it stretched the island's wartime jetty. Tower Rock is in profile in the background.

fish were taken to Cardiff market by the island's cutter. Mrs Davies's boats, furniture and animals were bought for £250 in July 1886 by Thomas Hall, formerly landlord of the Crown Inn at Glastonbury. He took over the island's tenancy from Mrs Davies, at a rent of £35 a year.

The next set of tenants about which much is known are the Sleemans. In 1909 James Sleeman and his 19-year-old son (also named James) came to the island to recover from tuberculosis. They were maltsters from Millend Mills, Eastington, Gloucestershire. They thought "the island life and sea air would do them good" and paid £30 a year rent. The rest of their family soon became entranced by Steep Holm and a sister, aunt and two other sons also moved to the island and made their home in the Barracks, living by farming and fishing. They kept a goat and a donkey.

Gradually the family drifted back to the mainland and when the younger James's health improved sufficiently, in 1912, he joined them. Their furniture and fishing and shooting tackle had been left in the Barracks. Early in 1914 word filtered through to Millend Mills that there had been a burglary on Steep Holm and the younger James landed with Pc Carter of Weston police to investigate. They found a different type of raider.

H. E. Landen, headmaster of Brynmelyn School at Coombe Road in Weston, had invaded the island for a botanical expedition with fifty of his pupils. Some of the boys were having joy-rides on the island's donkey and others were "carrying flowers in containers". Two of the island's three beds of Peony had been "wantonly damaged" and only the third, which was well-hidden, had escaped.

On a previous trip the same boys had swarmed over the cliffs and taken birds' eggs. As for the policeman, he had tea with Mr Landen and did not think the boys could do any damage "walking over the short grass". Sleeman, on the other hand, was furious, and successfully took out an injunction in Weston-super-Mare county court in July 1914 "restraining people from landing on the island without permission". He was awarded nominal damages of a shilling each against four Weston boatmen; John Baker, Henry Baker, W. Glover and Albert Counsell.

One aside at the hearing concerned the island's donkey and goat. An inspector for the National Society for the Prevention of Cruelty to Animals visited the island to see if there was sufficient food and water for the animals "but made no complaint about their condition".

In the 1930s the Wharton family leased Steep Holm to Harry Cox, an unpaid warden for the Royal Society for the Protection of Birds, who looked after the nature reserve on Brean Down. After Harry Cox died, in 1947, his executors retained the lease and allowed a few visiting parties of naturalists to use the island. The island was now regarded as a wildlife sanctuary, but doubts about its future were beginning to arise.

Baron Wharton's land in the West Country was 'settled' as a family trust with the London bankers Arthur and Edward Hoare appointed as trustees. Lord Wharton remained Steep Holm's tenant-for-life and in 1953 he firmly committed himself to the cause of conservation and rented the island to Harry Savory, Marie

Opposite: The Garden Cottage ruins on the top of the island, showing that the island's history of subsistence farming is at an end. In the changing attitudes of the 20th century, ecology was seen as the alternative.

Colthurst, Edmund Mason and Eric Kelting—representing an amalgam of the Bristol Naturalists Society, the Somerset Archaeological and Natural History Society, Folk House Archaeological Club and the Mid-Somerset Naturalists' Society. They paid £26 a year. Conditions were imposed. The island had to be preserved "as a sanctuary for birds and wildlife" and "nothing shall be done to damage the old emplacements and cannon". Archaeological finds had to be reported within fourteen days of their discovery and the tenants were required to "prepare and keep a catalogue of all such finds" which would "belong to and remain vested in the landlord". All the usual farming conditions and terms had now disappeared from the Steep Holm lease and the groups' involvement in the island was for "ecological and archaeological research" as well as education purposes. It was a comprehensive document and it opened the way for diversified studies, although these tended to centre on the Priory and the gulls.

Harry Savory died in 1962. Earlier in that year he had "cleared an appreciable amount of privet and sycamore from the Peony glens" and it was due to his efforts that the Peony survived in the changing ecology of the late 1950s. The results of his work were splendidly rewarded in the year he died: "The glens have produced the most magnificent display of blooms known for a very long time."

The final Baron Wharton—Charles John Halswell Kemeys-Tynte—was born on 12 January 1908 and died "without issue" at Mougins in the Alpes Maritimes, France, on 11 July 1969. His home had been in Lausanne, Switzerland. He directed in his will that his heart should be removed from his body and the corpse placed in a coffin to which "no lid is to be fitted". It was then cremated, and his ashes scattered or interred somewhere in England "other than at my family burial place in the county of Somerset" (the chapel at Halswell Park) without mourning or flowers. His principal beneficiary was Major Malcolm Ludovic Munthe, MC, of the Norwegian family of landscape painters. The Wharton line had ended.

After Lord Wharton's death, control of the island was held by Dorothy, Baroness Wharton. She was a veterinary surgeon living in Portugal and her principal interest in the island was also the survival of the Peony. She worried about excavations that had taken place at the Priory and decided she could only sell Steep Holm to an organisation capable of safeguarding the island's natural history. Tentative approaches were made to the existing island trust but no appeal was launched to raise money for the freehold. The National Trust, feeling the burden of its massive influx of coastal holdings that had resulted from Enterprise Neptune, was also approached but declined.

Baroness Wharton's agent, Nigel Murray, working in Yeovil, heard of the Kenneth Allsop Memorial Committee and its efforts to create a West Country nature reserve. The committee, established soon after Kenneth Allsop's death to establish a memorial in his name, negotiated to buy half of Eggardon Hill, a prehistoric fort on a chalkland escarpment near Bridport in Dorset. The owners refused to accept below £42,000 and even the fund's solicitor, Roger House, was prompted to ask—without being aware of the impending pun—"whether the money

Opposite: The island Barracks stands at the top of a scree slope overlooking the southern cliffs. It was built in 1867 and has become a study centre. The "bomb site" appearance of postwar days has been attacked on all fronts.

could not be spent along different channels altogether".

On 19 September, Nigel Murray phoned about Steep Holm. The committee— dismal about the mainland memorial prospects—was instantly revived. In the excitement a boat trip was arranged—and on 4 November 1973 John Percival, Mandy Allsop, Elizabeth and John Fowles and myself saw the island for the first time. Some initial impressions were recorded and may show how Steep Holm struck a party of visitors in the early 1970s:

"There is little evidence of any management work carried out on the island. No attempt has been made even to tidy up loose pieces of wartime ironwork. Members of the present island trust say that doubts about their future have not encouraged much recent work. It was disappointing, however, to find there is no organised volunteer labour force in existence. We heard of friction between archaeologists and gull ringers. The gull researchers have defended their terri- torial rights as ably as the gulls themselves. They stopped an excavation on the grounds that the dig was disturbing the birds. Obviously the extreme numbers of gulls (and not archaeologists) make the island unattractive for other rock-nesting birds. Though the island has been abandoned to nature since the war it is without noticeable worthwhile results. Rival introduced plants fight for space in the way any once-cultivated land reverts to an accidental type of wilderness far different from its primaeval state. There is no chance of the natural flora recovering as it is now extinct as far as the island is concerned."

John Percival, a television producer, summed it up: "It's the flora of the average British bomb-site with elder, privet and brambles." John Fowles pointed out that an examination of the Brean Down flora on the Somerset coast would pro- vide a list of plants that should have been expected on the island as well. The first essential task for conservationists moving into an unknown piece of land is to prepare lists of all the life that is there initially, but on Steep Holm much of the knowledge was passed on by a form of 20th century folklore.

Discussion showed there was great confusion over the plants, birds, insects and mammals different people claimed were present on the island. Despite the contra- dictions it was an encouraging day: "In every way the island is experiencing an eco- logical low, yet it has immense potential and could become a place of great beauty again, and attractive to every visitor to Weston-super-Mare."

John Fowles clinched the Allsop family's support for the island when he pre- sented Ken's widow, Betty, with a 'quasi-formal' outline of its three great assets: "Firstly, a breeding sanctuary and resting-place for migrants. Secondly as a site for an experiment, properly controlled, in improving an impoverished, unbalanced and already very 'corrupt' ecology. Thirdly an amenity site—a kind of true wildlife park—for nature-loving human visitors." He suggested organised visiting as the way to finance management of the island: "The atmosphere of the island contrives, because of all the old military paraphernalia, to be both very beautiful and very bizarre, and I see no reason at all why the public, paying a landing fee and kept

Opposite: Garden Cottage marks the western extremity of the area occupied by the island's medieval monks. There has been a pattern of shifting occupation for centuries. Some of the stone from the Priory is probably reused in its walls, and Garden Cottage was home for crofters and their animals.

within reasonable numbers, should be kept away as remorselessly as at present."

"I do hope the plunge is taken," he wrote. "For all its inscrutables, such a project seems to me in a way much closer to what Ken stood for than the buying of some piece of already reasonably 'safe' ground (such as Eggardon Hill) because of personal association. To me that would seem a little like a green gravestone. But somehow I think he would still be alive on Steep Holm, purely because it is a challenge, it does need work and energy and people to love it and take it in hand . . . and it could be such an exciting and worthwhile venture, both publicly and conservationally."

Betty Allsop (centre) with visitors inspecting clearance and renovation work carried out at Garden Cottage. The floors are being excavated as a preliminary to its eventual rebuilding. The island is being transformed into what John Fowles sees as a "true wildlife park".

The fund-raising started. Originally, the committee had come together as a section of Earth Resources Research, itself a charity wing of Friends of the Earth, and held meetings in London. Soon, with the island activities gathering momentum, the emphasis moved westward and the Kenneth Allsop Memorial Trust came into being as a separate body; Baroness Wharton realised appealing for money was a slow process and generously asked the Trust to manage Steep Holm as if the island were already bought.

She was particularly concerned that the Priory site should be properly preserved, and upset that it had been disturbed by past excavations. My own original connection with the Trust had been as negotiator trying to buy Eggardon Hill, and something may have been learned from the failure. I worded an additional clause for the Steep Holm sale contract, requiring the Trust "to request the Department of the Environment to schedule the Priory site for statutory protection under the

Ancient Monuments Act and whether or not the site is granted such legal protection the purchasers as trustees undertake to preserve the site as if it were their duty in law". Beric Morley, an inspector of Ancient Monuments, was eventually brought to the island and agreed to make the listing: "I am going to do as you suggest and schedule the Priory," he said. "I will include the ruined cottage and the ground to the west of it as there is a good chance that the mediaeval buildings covered a larger area."

Baroness Wharton also asked for a stone from the island as a memento. That request was never met, for very sadly the *Times* carried her obituary a few days

Archaeology, Steep Holm style. The trench has revealed a George III cannon at Garden Battery. It had been completely covered during the Second World War. A pillar (right) erected in memory of naturalist Harry Cox, stands in the filled barbette.

later. The committee were naturally very apprehensive about the future, but Steep Holm has been lucky in its heirs, and the next was no exception. The Hon. Mrs Ziki Robertson, Lady Wharton's daughter and the new owner, was totally in favour of the Trust's efforts. Her husband, the composer Harry Robertson, was also keenly in support.

On 3 August they came with their family to see the island. The encouragement was not only verbal, but included a substantial reduction in the island's purchase price. When the deal was completed Ziki Robertson joined us as a trustee.

In its first two full years of running the island, the Trust took nearly a thousand visitors to Steep Holm. More than 500 birds were ringed. Numerous work parties embarked on a mammoth programme to make the island's historical features visually more presentable. Their work on Split Rock battery, involving the removal of tons of Second World War brick and tile debris, won praise from the visiting Ancient Monuments inspector: "It's an impressive transformation. Everything was hidden on our last visit. There's not much more I can ask you to do."

Groups working on the restoration project included the International Voluntary Service, Forest School Camps, Sidcot School, several teams of guides and Weston Sea Cadets. A high proportion were girls and most of the volunteers were aged between 13 and 20. Perhaps their greatest achievement was the removal of more than 2,500 cubic feet of stone and earth to expose an entirely covered Victorian gun emplacement at Garden Battery. The filling had been dumped there in 1941, and its clearance involved moving the heavy wartime concrete pillar on which a brass memorial plate to Harry Cox is fixed. This now stands beside the barbette, a far more attractive setting. The work won an award of merit in the Better Britain Competition.

A distinguished graphical designer Michael Harvey of Bridport, carved a plaque in Welsh slate to commemorate Kenneth Allsop and the buying of the island. The stone he used was lifted from a Victorian prison floor. Apparently this is now the best way of acquiring a large slab of high-quality slate. Weighing about 80 pounds, it was mounted single-handedly by the Trust's engineer, Michael Yesson, on the vertical wall of Cliff Cottage, facing eastward and out to sea. It has as its emblem a Peregrine and records: "This island of Steep Holm was bought by public subscription in the year 1976 to preserve the memory of the writer and naturalist KENNETH ALLSOP, 1920-1973."

The Trust committee hopes one day to plant a bed of Wild Peony beneath it.

Several tons of earth and stone were removed to reveal (left) the Victorian western barbette at Garden Battery. A memorial pillar to Harry Cox also had to be moved. The symbol of a Peregrine falcon (right) appears on the slate in memory of Kenneth Allsop, cut by Michael Harvey and erected at Cliff Cottage by Michael Yesson.

The Palmerston Follies

Rodney Legg

IN 1867 a determined effort was made to throw an effective gun barrage across the ten-mile wide approaches to the ports of Bristol and Cardiff. Seven-ton guns, guarding the neck of the Bristol Channel, became part of a national assortment of coastal defence works collectively dubbed "Palmerston's Follies".

They took their name from the former Prime Minister, Viscount Palmerston, and were follies because during the 1860s Europe turned from a turbulent phase of politics into a quiet one with no reasons for fearing an invasion of Britain. Palmerston died in 1865 and three years later his massive fortifications were still being completed.

When their plans were drawn, the danger seemed real. The French had begun rapid construction of ironclad ships and by 1859, at the outbreak of the Franco-Austrian war, there were widespread rumours of imminent war between France and Britain. Sidney Herbert presented the British cabinet with a contingency plan assuming it had happened. Steep Holm was garrisoned as a result of the 1860 Royal Commission on the Defence of the United Kingdom, its greatest creations being the chains of landward forts protecting the naval bases of Chatham, Portsmouth and Plymouth.

The two mainland strong-points of the Bristol Channel barrier were Lavernock near Barry, in South Wales, and Brean Down at the western extremity of Somerset's Mendip Hills. Effective blocking of the estuary was only possible because of the existence, halfway across, of Flat Holm and Steep Holm. The latter, of all four fortified points, is by far the best preserved, with the distinction of being the only Victorian heavy battery in the British Isles that still has its guns.

Before the 1860s it was not possible to bar a ten-mile channel by land defences alone. The cannon was at last turned into a devastating weapon and underwent more changes in the 1860s than in all the centuries since the first making of gunpowder. Outwardly, the appearance of the guns was transformed from the long, slender look of the past to a shape which is clumsy, fat and bulbous. The new guns appear pregnant.

In action they were murderous. Guns of this type were invented by a West Point graduate, Robert Parker Parrott, who left the American army to run a foundry. In 1861 he perfected a method of strengthening the existing cast-iron guns by shrinking wrought-iron hoops on the breech. They could now take a far greater charge and at the same time Parrot introduced an expanding projectile for rifled cannon. Production went ahead immediately, and Parrott guns were used by the Union army against Confederate forces throughout the Civil War, which lasted until 1865.

Details of Parrott's two gun patents were soon being studied on this side of the Atlantic by engineers Sir William Armstrong (inventor of the breech loader) and Sir Joseph Whitworth (who standardised screw threads). Whitworth experimented with hexagonal rifling in muzzle-loaded guns. An elongated projectile was then used to increase the range and precision of fire. Traditional cannon balls had become a thing of the past. They were replaced by cartridges devised by Major William Palliser.

Lynall Thomas suggested in Britain that Parrott's wrapping of a strengthened tube around the exteriors of the guns could be improved upon. The wrought-iron element should be at the centre to receive the initial impact. Palliser, improving his reputation as a scientific artillerist (he was later knighted) placed the wrought-iron tube in the middle of the gun and found this "added enormously to the strength". Thomas made the world's first 7-inch gun—of steel and forged in one piece, "the largest which had ever been attempted"—but the breech burst with its second trial charge.

In 1865 the Royal Gun Factory at Woolwich made its first heavy rifled muzzle-loaders and they evolved into the massive seven-ton barrels that lie on Steep Holm. These guns, the Mark III, were designed for land service and were standard issue for most forts, with a production run of about 500. Fifty-one had been made of the Mark I, but only two prototypes of the Mark II, and the Mark III differed in being constructed by the Frazer method, a simplified variant of Armstrong's original design. Both the Mark I and Mark III have an inner tube of tough steel, but the Mark II used a tube of coiled iron instead.

Mark III—the gun that went into service—has a calibre of seven inches, an overall length of 12 feet 4 inches, and a bore of 10 feet 6 inches. The maximum external diameter, at the breech end, is 2 feet 7 inches. Inside, the rifling consists of "three grooves, 1.5 inch wide and .18 inch deep, with a uniform twist of one turn in 35 calibres". The groove was rounded off at both sides, a Woolwich refinement, as this prevented the steel splitting along the edges. Two studs, projecting from the muzzle of several of the Steep Holm guns, were locating pegs for a cradle or tray. The shell was placed onto this and correctly aligned with the rifling of the gun.

The guns took a 30 lb charge of gunpowder and fired 112 lb Palliser cylindrical shot at 1,560 feet per second. This could puncture eight inches of iron at a dis-

Opposite: A Parrott-style gun on Steep Holm, at Tombstone Battery, weighing seven tons and representing the final generation of muzzle loaders. It was made in 1869 and is numbered 81.

tance of 1,000 yards.

Eight of these huge guns survive on Steep Holm, though on the mainland cannon of this type are now virtually unknown. Overseas there are only isolated colonial specimens; reputedly on Malta and one or two on Ascension Island in the South Atlantic. Similar guns have been removed from Flat Holm, and Steep Holm now has the only intact collection. Their rarity was confirmed by a Department of the Environment official in 1974 whose report stressed "the very great importance placed upon the muzzle-loading gun barrels that survive on the island." Preservation is urged: "These (cannon) are indeed rare and should be cherished as if they were ancient monuments." Historically, the significance of the guns of Steep Holm is that they were among the largest and last muzzle-loaders ever made. Size with these guns is a relative matter, and cannon of the same basic shape were built to 80 tons and exist on Malta and Gibralter. Nothing of this enormous weight was thought to have survived in Britain, but in 1976 port construction workers at Dover uncovered an 80-ton gun in its original emplacement. Unlike the Steep

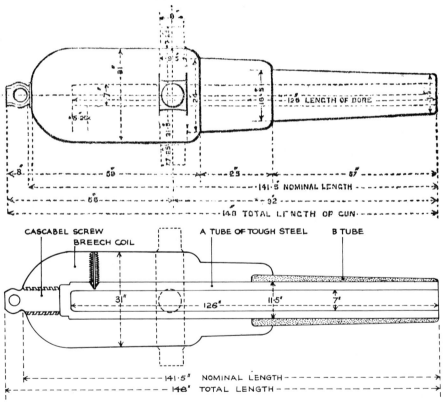

Contemporary drawings give the dimensions of "the wrought iron muzzle-loading 7-inch gun of 7 tons, Mark III". These figures have been compared with the eight Victorian gun barrels on Steep Holm and apply in each case.

Holm cannon, which were revolved manually, the Dover gun was pulled around its mounting by a steam engine.

Each Steep Holm barrel has 38 lines incised for aiming purposes, while the left trunnion carries the proofing date and Woolwich serial number. The coding on the western gun at Split Rock, for example, reads: "RGF No.86, III, 1868". It was made at the Royal Gun Factory; is a Mark III barrel; was tested with heavy proof rounds in 1868 (to ensure the casing would withstand a charge); and has the works number 86 (the Steep Holm batch run partly in sequence). The west gun at Summit Battery is number 87 of 1868. Other visible trunnions have the year 1869 and the numbers 72 (Tombstone Battery, west), 81 (Tombstone, east), 85 (Laboratory Battery). The east gun at Summit Battery is number 97 but its date is unclear. At the centre of each gun, on the top, is Queen Victoria's cipher and the wording "HONI SOIT QUI MAL Y PENSE"–the motto of the Order of the Garter, in mediaeval French, meaning "shame on him who thinks evil of it". The letters are surmounted by St Edward's crown. The details stamped on the guns are reasonably visible in cases where the appropriate part of the gun is exposed, particularly if rubbed with moist leaves.

Remarkably, despite being in the salt air for a century, the guns are well preserved and brown only from a light surface rusting. The toughened casing successfully resists corrosion, unlike the younger but rapidly flaking ironwork from the Second World War, which is in an advanced stage of disintegration all over the island. Even the heavy armour-plated doors of generator houses have rusted away.

Six substantial emplacements were built on Steep Holm in 1867, prior to the arrival of the guns, and a barracks for 50 men. The twin battery at Split Rock is particularly impressive, poised dramatically on the edge of a 200-foot craggy cliff, with a view to Exmoor, Lundy (if only on the clearest days) and the Atlantic. It is complete still, with an underground powder-room beneath each gun, and is a feasible

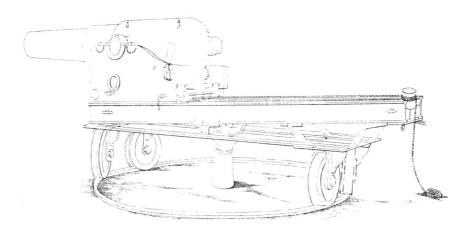

This type of platform was used for mounting the Steep Holm cannon. It turned on rails and weighed as much as the gun itself.

proposition for restoration. Each storeroom is reached by a flight of steps at the rear of the emplacement and has a shaft leading up to the guns. Ceiling the room is a dome of vaulted brick and the walls still keep dry. The Victorian guns were mounted on a seven-ton obsolete iron "dwarf platform" of the C-pivot type ('C' standing for the George III cannon set intact and upright into the base of each emplacement).

One of these earlier Georgian guns, displaced from the east barbette of Summit Battery, lies behind the Second World War 6-inch gun emplacement there. It is a cast-iron smooth-bore 32 pounder of the Napoleonic period, dated about 1800, and ten feet long. Similar guns were placed at the top of Martello towers. The left trunnion carries the maker's initials "W Co"—standing for Walker and Company of Rotherham, Ironfounders to the Board of Ordnance—and on the right trunnion the number 229. This gun has a 6.1/8-inch bore and fired a muzzle-loaded cannon ball. Clearance of soil from around the breech would give the weight of the gun, chiselled beneath the cascabel. Also at Summit Battery, from the same destroyed barbette, there is part of the 1869 gun's racer—the circular rail on which the gun platform ran—lying in an old railway cutting. It has massive three-feet wide claws set about three feet apart and this and the size of the Georgian cannon shows the amount of underground shock-resistance built into the Steep Holm emplacements.

The inside face of the protective barbette is a semi-circular wall of faced ashlar, rough tooled at the centre of each block to a uniform design, and outwards a ramp of earth and stone slopes down to merge with the upper scree of the cliff. Behind the rear of the Split Rock emplacements runs a wide railway cutting which was cleared in 1975 of bushes and the debris from Second World War buildings by a team of International Voluntary Service workers. A less unsightly sign of military continuity was preserved. At the top of the battery, between the two semi-circular barbettes, is a concrete pad and circle of iron rods on which an anti-aircraft gun was mounted during the Second World War to fire at German bombers returning from Cardiff.

Underground, the magazine chambers in different parts of the island show considerable variations in layout. Ten survive intact (including the western one at Summit Battery, completely filled with 1941 rubble until it was dug out by a Forest School Camp in 1977). The pair at Rudder Rock have passages leading to an end chamber. Above the inner door of the southern magazine the woodwork still has its Victorian painted wording: "CARTRIDGE STORE FOR 7 in. GUN." The northern magazine has the word "Shell" instead of "Cartridge".

Top: Left trunnion of a Steep Holm gun (Split Rock Battery, west). "R.G.F." stands for "Royal Gun Factory". "No. 86" is its proofing number. "III" stands for the Mark of the barrel. "1868" is its date. Seldom is history more obliging.
Bottom left: Queen Victoria's cipher, cast into the top of the gun barrel at Summit battery (east). 'V.R.'' are the initials at the centre, encircled by the motto of the Order of the Garter: "HONI SOIT QUI MAL Y PENSE". The crest is surmounted by St Edward's crown.
Bottom right: The underside is now uppermost in the case of Victorian gun barrel No. 85 at Split Rock Battery. The lines total 38 and were for aiming purposes. The gun's cascabel screw is in the foreground. Its total length is 148 inches.

The twin pair of magazines at Split Rock are fundamentally different, with the steps opening directly into the powder store. Here there are even unexpected differences between the rooms and one is longer than the other. In several of the chambers there are thick deposits of white snow-like efflorescent crystals leeched from the red brick. These layers do not dissolve in the dark, cool conditions, and similar accumulations have been found at the foot of walls in brick funeral vaults in London.

Considerable engineering works were necessary on the island before a start could be made hauling guns, equipment and supplies up the cliffs. Operations on Steep Holm must have encountered severe physical difficulties at every stage. A stone jetty was built to the low-water mark near Calf Rock and an incline terrace constructed from this South Landing to the top of the island. Rails were laid along a single, straight slope and a Victorian winch survives amongst privet bushes at the head. Metals and sleepers are still in place but probably date from 1941. There is a well preserved limekiln at the bottom and another, ruined, at the top, behind a 1941 generator building. Stone for facing the Steep Holm constructions was brought from the mainland, already shaped into squared-up blocks, although considerable quantities of rubble were produced from railway cuttings towards the west end of the island. There was no attempt to supplement this source of supply by opening an island quarry of any size, much of the stone blown out from behind the Barracks site being used to consolidate its own slope.

Water for the mixing of mortar for the construction of the Barracks and the gun emplacements was collected by an ingenious method. A cave in a haematite vein above the high water mark just over a hundred yards west from the South Landing limekiln narrows to a continuing passage rising into the island. Down it runs a steady flow of fresh water.

The bottom of this cave—known now as Reservoir Cavity—was dammed in 1867 with stone to hold back the water. A winching point was built, again in stone, on the cliff edge above. It is a small square tower set into the slope. Two vertical grooves, built into the southern face, controlled ropes.

Linking the top of the tower with the limekiln there was a smoothly levelled trackway, about eight feet wide, which gradually descended, following the natural slant of the clifftop, to the limekiln. This track, which could have carried a railway line, is still well defined, despite rockfalls and minor landslips, and can be traced on the ground and from aerial photographs. As it arrives at the South Landing area it passes directly to the north of the ruined wartime hut which stands behind the searchlight post.

In front of the searchlight post and running for about 60 feet west of it there is a curtain wall of stone—five feet high at the west end and 15 feet high at the east—behind which the ground has been embanked and platformed. Comparison between the masonry of this wall and the tower, which for clarity is now called the Water

Opposite: "CARTRIDGE STORE FOR 7in. GUN" is still stencilled in Victorian lettering above the inner door of this underground magazine at Rudder Rock. Outside there is an ashlar frontage, but inside the roofs are constructed with arched brickwork. The walls have graffiti from the last war.

Above: Centre, at the top of the cliff, is the Water Haul. This 1867 structure held the ropes that lifted water from a small cave, Reservoir Cavity, that had been dammed at the foot of the cliff (in the darker patch, beneath the mini-tower, dead centre of picture). Sufficient water came from here for the initial building work.

Opposite: South landing: the logistics of the military takeover of Steep Holm in 1867 necessitated construction of a stone jetty into the sea below Tower Rock. The stone wall supporting the searchlight post (1941) is also Victorian. From this platform a winch-operated cable railway hauled supplies to the top.

Haul, shows that all the work is Victorian. It is on this man-made platform, which counteracts the natural tilt of the cliff towards the east, that both the searchlight post and hut are built. But both of these date from the last war. The site they occupy is older, but may never have had buildings. It seems to have been the mixing area for mortar, and assembling stonework and weapons for loading into railway trucks to go up the Incline Railway to the top of the island. During the Victorian period this was the only railway up the island cliffs and the degree of military occupation means that materials totalling thousands of tons had to be unloaded from barges and transferred to rail trucks. That such trouble was taken to build a level loading-bay is an indication that the smooth gradient to the Water Haul is not accidental, but was constructed to carry a set of rails.

Its width and straightness suggests there may have been two parallel lengths of rail—loaded trucks descending on one pulling the empty trucks back to the top along the other. This was a common system for those incline railways where the loads were being sent downhill.

On the top of the island a conventional mule-drawn tramway was constructed to the south-west point of the island, above Rudder Rock. An extension was then built eastward from the winch above the Incline Railway, across the old Priory garden, and from there westward along the entire length of the northern cliffs to a cutting behind Summit Battery. Much of its course is today the island's perimeter path. However, the railway was never continuous as the severe slope prevented Rudder Rock and Summit Batteries from ever being connected. Rudder Rock was the terminus for the southern line, and Summit Battery the end of the northern line.

The other major project was the building of the Barracks. A shelf had to be blasted into the island's southern slopes, but before this there would have been surveys. The Barracks siting can hardly be accidental, and water may be the key to its location.

Immediately north of the building is an underground reservoir, also built in 1867, holding 49,000 gallons. Rainwater runs down a rock face, through a carbon

Opposite: Warworks at Tombstone Battery, dating from 1868. The steps lead into an underground magazine. Ten such batteries were built, each to hold a seven-inch gun (right) and eight of the barbettes and guns survive.
Below: Limekiln at South Landing, built to provide mortar for the island's 1867-69 "Palmerston Folly" constructions. A second limekiln was built on the top of the island.

filter-bed, into brick tanks. Colin Rogers, leader of the Axbridge Caving Group, doubts whether the quantity of water seeping from Steep Holm rock could maintain a supply of this size. He suggested in 1975 that the explanation lay in a well-known hydrological phenomenon and that the principal intake of water to the tank comes not from the top but the bottom. Rogers argues that water falling on to the Mendip Hills runs through the rocks under the Bristol Channel and emerges in the centre of Steep Holm. He points out that there is seepage from the lower cliffs of Steep Holm whereas Brean Down promontory, similar in size, is dry. Small caves exist on the Steep Holm cliffs in a direct line with the Barracks at Window Cave (to the south) and Jubilee Cave (on the northern cliffs). These openings peter out but there is a possibility that smaller passages run through the centre of the island. In 1976, with the driest and hottest summer on record, the weather provided what must be the strongest possible support for Rogers' theory. Throughout August, a month when many mainland wells and water supplies ran dry, there was still more than five feet of water in the island's reservoir. The island had not received any rainfall, and if anything looked more parched and withered than the opposite coasts, but the underground water level remained static. Moisture continued to ooze from the rocks below the mediaeval well and around Jubilee Cave at the north-east side of the island. The main part of the sycamore wood above the beach entirely lost its leaves by the beginning of September 1976 but the trees, brambles and ivy north and west of Cliff Cottage—in this area of water seepage—not only retained their leaves but remained fully green. Boatmen in the Bristol Channel have noticed points near Steep Holm where freshwater bubbles to the surface and disturbs the mud on the seabed.

Steep Holm's military history was uneventful between the completion of works in 1868 and one brief interlude of significance near the end of Victoria's reign. The garrison was cut to only a few men, and in 1898 the War Office chose Steep Holm for a test that was to establish its own obsolescence. Breech-loading guns were now replacing cannon and in 1898 the Admiralty decided to see whether the new guns could be put into existing barbettes with metal shields for additional protection. This had the advantage of being considerably cheaper than making new emplacements. Rudder Rock, at the west point of the island, was chosen for the exercise. A dummy 9.2-inch breech-loader was placed in a specially-made 'tortoise' shield of nickel steel 34 feet from end to end. This metal was three inches thick, of the type used for armoured plate in battleships, from a process invented in America by Hayward Augustus Harvey. It had seven per cent nickel to give it extra strength. The tortoise-shape was chosen so that the surface curving inwards would offer least resistance and deflect shot. The front was oval and the whole shield moved on wheels, running on the racer of the 1868 emplacement.

The shield and barbette at Rudder Rock were pounded by HMS *Arrogant*, a second-class cruiser, using her whole armament of 6-inch, 4.7-inch and smaller guns. The *Arrogant* was a twin screw ship laid down on 26 May 1896 and built at Devonport. She was 320 feet long with 5,000 tons displacement, and was to survive the First World War, being broken up at Blyth in 1923.

What happened is reported in the *Naval and Military Records* for 25 August 1898: "After many days the *Arrogant*, steaming at about ten knots in the teeth

Observers of the 'Arrogant' firing watched from Summit Battery, and signalled hits to the ship. Today's background, however, is a 1941 6-inch gun emplacement. Foreground is a displaced Victorian cannon, seen from what was originally its top.

of wind at a distance of 1,800 yards from Steep Holm fired four of her starboard guns in quick succession, clouds of dust being seen to rise from the rock in the vicinity of the battery, though, so far as binoculars could reveal, no flash hits were made. Indeed experts declared that it would need almost magnificent gunnery to drop a shot on the battery, so great its elevation above sea level.

"As the *Arrogant* swept past her big 6-in. gun was brought into range, the weapon going off with a deafening roar, then the *Arrogant* steamed slowly round the island. As it reached its south-western extremity a heavy report was heard from (observers at) the Summit Battery, which was generally regarded as a signal that no hit upon the shield had been made.

"Again the cruiser shaped her course past the battery and again she fired and thus the firing continued from eight o'clock until noon. The earlier stages of the experimental firing, namely for about the first two hours, appeared to have been carried out with guns of a smaller calibre, for so far no effect was produced upon the target or breast-work of the fort.

"Towards noon however, some of the heavier defence ordnance were brought into use and these quickly made their effect felt, for so far as spectators at a distance could observe a portion of the shield was blown away causing the gun to be exposed and the surrounding structure to be reduced to a mere heap of rubbish. It is estimated that nearly 200 shells were fired from the cruiser. Shortly after mid-day the firing ceased and the *Arrogant* returned to her anchorage." The report is unclear in its reference to "heavier defence ordnance"—land guns—which it suggests the cruiser was carrying. Her own armament had nothing heavier than the 6-inch gun which she was already using.

Because of the "historical significance of the site" the Department of the Environment announced in 1975 it was scheduling the Rudder Rock battery as an ancient monument and added: "The remains of the shattered 'tortoise-shell' are very much part of the monument in their existing positions." This scheduling allowed Steep Holm to claim the contradictory superlative "the youngest ancient monument in Britain", though only temporarily as the Department has now listed a Second World War tank trap in Dorset.

Modern warfare, by the turn of the century, was leaving Steep Holm behind. The garrison was not re-armed with breech-loaders and its military life must have seemed near to a close. Inevitably, in 1903, the War Office finally abandoned the island. The great obsolete guns were sold to a Cardiff scrap merchant. He found them too heavy to move and attempted cutting but failed to break them into pieces.

Rusted relics of the 'Arrogant' incident. The twisted steel (centre left) is all that remains of the tortoise-shaped armoured shield of the 1898 gun test. To its right is a George III cannon muzzle, and the island's 1941 Battery Observation Post.

One gun at Garden Battery was attacked with determination and became increasingly resistant as the cutter approached the centre and "the intensely hard inner lining of the bore". Something may have been taken back to Cardiff, however, as all the mountings for the guns have completely disappeared.

Two of the guns may also have vanished. Apparently, ten were brought to the island in 1868-69, but there are only eight now. Considering these defied scrap merchants, it is probable that if the other two ever reached Steep Holm, they are still there today. Possibly, they were covered with debris or used as foundations when the second generation of Steep Holm defences was built to shield the Channel. Second World War concrete and iron constructions displaced the neat stonework of the Victorian emplacements at Summit, Rudder Rock and Garden batteries, though the remaining three (Split Rock, Tombstone and Laboratory) are not superimposed by 1940 defences.

Garden Battery's concrete may well hide one of the lost guns. Originally this was a twin emplacement and its eastern barbette was destroyed in the building of a substantial 1940 battery. A displaced Victorian cannon lies to the rear of the concrete blockhouse but the second Victorian cannon of Garden Battery is missing. One mounting point, the western barbette, was filled with soil and stone rubble from the site of the adjacent excavations in 1940, but was cleared in 1976 to reveal its circular rail and Georgian gun-pivot. No Victorian barrel was found. It is likely that this was the gun that was said in 1938 to be cut in two, and that these pieces are embedded in the concrete footings of the wartime 6 inch battery.

Even the present distribution of the remaining eight guns is intriguing. There are pairs of Parrott guns at or near Summit, Tombstone and Split Rock batteries and a single one at Garden and Laboratory batteries. The other two batteries, Rudder Rock and Observatory, have no guns. Yet Rudder Rock must have had a gun as it is the most strategically placed of all six batteries, at the very tip of the projecting westerly end of the island; and as it figured in the *Arrogant* affair, can be assumed to have functioned. Enough later activity, including the building of a searchlight post on the side of Rudder Rock, has taken place to hide the gun. A metal detector might find it, and while the sub-surface litter of ironwork is considerable, a lump weighing seven tons should register a stronger signal. A sea magnet may also be necessary as the precipitous cliff on the north side of Rudder Rock is the only place in the entire island where anything pushed over the edge will fall into deep water. This could have been the most tempting method of disposal. If a missing gun is found here, one other problem will remain.

Was Observatory battery ever built? It is emphatically shown in outline on the

Page 116 Scene of the 1898 gun-shield test, though Rudder Rock was then without its searchlight post and steps (they date from the Second World War). This is Steep Holm at its most impressive, photographed to show how the sea has cut a series of arches through the end of the island.

Page 117 Superbly preserved, the twin Victorian 7-inch gun batteries at Split Rock were made presentable in 1975 by volunteers working for the Kenneth Allsop Trust. Masses of rubble from the last war had to be cleared from behind the barbettes. Strategically sited, the guns had wide arc of fire and covered the northern coasts of Somerset and Devon.

large rolled masterplan of the island housed in the Public Record Office, and located halfway along the north face of the island, almost equal distance between Summit and Tombstone batteries. On this map, however, a question mark is added after the name, and a comment at the foot of the map—"subject to survey"— applies to both Observatory and Summit batteries. On the ground at the former, there are not only no guns, but no sign of any emplacements, or of later work to displace them.

The presumption must be that Observatory battery was never started, and militarily it would have been the least necessary of all, as it is well covered by the arcs of fire from both Summit and Tombstone guns. Anyway, the distance along the southern shore between Split Rock and Garden batteries is appreciably longer than that separating Summit from Tombstone. The Barracks is at the middle of the southern side but cannot be counted as a fighting or even defensive structure. The negative evidence for no Observatory battery is that the five known sets of emplacements can account for all ten of the island's guns.

Explanations of Steep Holm's original military layout have to be supported by reference to the Victorian plans. Twentieth century maps and accounts have introduced inaccuracy and confusion. Tombstone battery, for instance, was so-called because a broken mediaeval coffin lid was built into the wall of a nearby side-arms store. The name has since been erroneously transferred to Garden Battery to the south of the Priory ruins, where a Victorian cannon lies at the foot of a Second World War emplacement. The original Tombstone battery was re-named Laboratory battery, a name no one has been able to explain. In this account, as you go clockwise around the island, the batteries have been named Rudder Rock, Summit, Observatory (no trace), Tombstone, Laboratory, Garden and Split Rock.

Among the lesser military relics on Steep Holm are carved stone boundary posts. These are of Palmerstonian rather than Second War vintage and were intended to show the extent of military occupation. Politics meant the Admiralty had to be seen to be acquiring only the minimum area of land essential for its needs. Each gun battery plot was therefore carefully squared up and marked out. On Steep Holm the exercise was meaningless, as the whole island had to be used in various ways, but it was a regulation that was carried out all the same. In 1941 the army had the island to itself.

The Victorian opinion of the island's strategic capabilities was to be endorsed in 1941 by the planners of the Steep Holm Second World War anti-invasion works. The check was on shipping and aircraft heading towards Bristol and Cardiff. The Western ports had a new importance as London and the South-East succumbed to virtual siege conditions. In 1941-44, the passage between the two Holms (the name means 'islands') of the Bristol Channel was the defended gateway to Britain and a symbol of relief for those who had survived the treacherous South-Western Approaches. It also had a practical role in covering the sea outside Cardiff Docks, and protecting the assembling and dispersal of convoys of merchant ships.

Hitler's war

Rodney Legg

UNCOMFORTABLE MEMORIES of Steep Holm's war years are held by those who served on the island, and in particular amongst the men who carried out its initial re-fortification. The work was undertaken by 930 Port Construction and Repair Company of the Royal Engineers, formed in the spring of 1941 under the command of Major D. P. Bertlin.

S. G. Rock, who kept the company's war diary, describes it as "a technical company with a high proportion of territorials and reserve personnel who, in peace-time, were engaged in the civil engineering industry, specialising in works of marine construction".

In 1941 they built jetties and fortifications at Steep Holm, Flat Holm, Brean Down, Drake's Island at Plymouth, and in the Clyde estuary. The work at Steep Holm began in July 1941 and was to last until October 1942. In the Bristol Channel operations the company was based at Barry Dock and Major Bertlin requisitioned a small coastal steamer of about 300 tons, *mv Assurity,* owned by Everards of Greenhithe and on charter to the War Department. She was unsuitable for laying moorings and another smaller motor barge from Greenwich, *mv Peter Piper,* was used, as she was fitted with a heavy derrick and dropped a large concrete block on to the bed of the Channel off Steep Holm. A chain was attached to the block at one end, and a steel floating buoy at the other. The buoy had a mooring shackle.

"Our task was to fortify the islands to repel any possible enemy force coming up the Bristol Channel," Major Bertlin recalls. "Because of the steep path to the top of Steep Holm, mules were landed on the beach by tank landing craft and I planned a zig-zag railway to haul the guns up the steep cliff. We also built a high-water jetty using standard military trestle-pier building units."

The footings of the wartime jetty were visible for a week in October 1976. The sea had scoured the beach of loose stones and exposed the smaller pebbles, firmly embedded in clay, which lie below. The jetty foundation—steel tubes set into concrete in two regular lines—ran due east from the 1941 beach-side stone wall, towards low water mark on the southern side of the spit, or 'cassey' as it is called by boat-men. Within days, gales and equinoctial flood tides swept hundreds of tons of stone back on to the beach, and its relics of the 1941 operation were hidden again beneath three feet of pebbles.

Two types of equipment were in use for jetty construction, known as L-type and V-type trestling, and it appears the former was used on Steep Holm beach. "Both were constructed on the 'Meccano' principle," Mr Rock says, "the steelwork being prefabricated and pre-drilled for speedy erection and bolting under war con-ditions. Due to the tidal conditions in the Bristol Channel, the jetty was constructed so it dried out at low water. It was useable only around high water."

Those who actually carried out the physical work remember with less enthusiasm. "When we landed on Steep Holm, the only occupants were seagulls and the largest earwigs I have ever seen," says Harold Parr of Catford. "We were under canvas and although it was a sweltering summer we slept wearing Balaclava helmets to keep the monsters out of our hair. In the morning there was always a ball of earwigs, bigger than one's fist, up the top of the tent poles.

"Little time was lost over meals because we were only fed on bully-beef and biscuits. Breakfast was porridge made from biscuits, and we had no bread. If the

The Royal Engineers arrive at Steep Holm in July 1941. The first sappers and their equipment have been beached. The island's inn (right) still stands to three storeys, but only for another two weeks. Photo: A. Harden.

boat was weather-bound in Barry we went without our ration of cigarettes and chocolate. Non-smokers sold their Woodbines at sixpence each. Conditions were bad, unnecessarily so."

This view is echoed by Bert Harden of Westcliff-on-Sea: "Building the jetty on Steep Holm and carving an approach road up the cliffs, along an old rabbit run, proved to be one of the hardest tasks we ever had to tackle and we had to be pushed to the limits of human endeavour in order to complete on schedule in the foulest conditions imaginable. We built our jetty and road on Steep Holm, as did our other section on Flat Holm, at a cost of four men dead. Soon afterwards we were in Africa, and from there to Salerno and Anzio, followed by D-day in Normandy. What followed almost erased the memory of the starvation and misery of those days on Steep Holm, though our experience helped us to overcome everything we met later in the war.

"Despite recurring periods of near starvation and sickness, men worked from dawn to dusk every day and once a month we were allowed ashore for 48 hours for baths and medical inspection. I was doing a lot of diving and underwater work during one period and at low tide we would work waist-deep in water, causing cramp in my legs. I told the doctor, who advised me to have an occasional beneficial

'Assurity' unloads steel girders for jetty-building. This picture was taken on Flat Holm, but on Steep Holm too the principle was the same. The 300 ton steamer was driven as far up the beach as possible, her load being removed as the tide ebbed. Photo: H. Parr.

paddle in salt water. I'd done nothing else for weeks on end."

The problem with supplying Steep Holm was that stores had to be unloaded at high tide, when often a strong race runs across the east beach. *Assurity* was only capable of about four knots and the tide off the tip of the island often moves at over six knots. "It needed nerves of steel to bring her close enough to unload stores," Mr Harden pointed out. "Many times she failed, and left us starving and desperate, returning to the mainland with everything we longed for.

"Our senior officers on the island were Captain 'Black' Morgan and Lieutenant Peter Hopper, a Canadian veteran from the First World War. He was dubbed 'Two-gun Pete' as he carried two low-slung revolvers strapped to his thighs. Once, when we had gone without proper food for at least ten days, and supplemented our rations with gull eggs, birds and rabbits, *Assurity* was standing off-shore in the lee of a gale, waiting for calmer waters in order to unload. After several attempts at coming in without being dashed against the cliffs, the skipper—who was a relief man—informed us he was returning to Barry.

"At this, 'Two-gun Pete' whipped out a revolver and threatened to blow the skipper's head off if he didn't bring the ship in. Even that was to no avail, and we had to wait for our regular skipper to return two days later."

Mr Parr, a company lighterman, was involved in the carrying of supplies. The method of unloading in the early stages of the military occupation was to run in onto the beach as far as possible, and then throw all the steelwork overboard. This was retrieved when the water ebbed. The boat itself, after dropping its load of metal, had to be warped back a length on its stern anchor, and kept afloat whilst the rest of the cargo was ferried ashore in a couple of ships' lifeboats. After a time the *Peter Piper* was withdrawn, and the island men had the use of a Bristol dumb-barge, *Yumbi*, which was towed from Barry. Mr Parr was responsible for her: "I had to moor her, ground her, and then see that the aft-end of the barge was emptied before the tide came back—otherwise she wouldn't have lifted, lying as she did on such an angled, sloping beach."

It is Mr Parr who has solved the mystery of the island's wartime water supply. As Steep Holm never suffers any shortage of underground water, it seemed inconceivable to be told that amongst all its other problems 930 Port Construction and Repair Company had to bring drinking water in four-gallon cans from Barry. Elaborate stage-tanks were constructed on concrete platforms, one beside the railway at the east end of Cliff Cottage, and another two on the top of the island to the south of the Ordnance Survey pillar.

Top: John Watts (right) is the island's ferryman. Some German prisoners are said to have been taken to Steep Holm which, as John points out, is "not the sort of place you can escape from". A concrete grid (left), at Cliff Cottage, held water tanks after the island's own water supply had been contaminated. Drinking water had to come from Barry.
Bottom: Rediscovered, through information from men who served on Steep Holm during the war, this is the island's mediaeval well. It has a wartime iron lid but was soon abandoned. Somehow this (or the Barracks water supply) became polluted and caused a typhoid outbreak. After 1945 a ton of scree slipped across the top. Phil Howell is first to re-explore.

The 1941 face of South Landing—searchlight and Nissen hut. The island was ringed with lights and challenged shipping. A donkey engine pulled skips up the railway line.

The explanation, according to Mr Parr, is that the men were drinking water from the island's water-tank behind the barracks, or alternatively from the ancient cliff-side well below the Priory, which was rebuilt and given an iron lid. There was then some sickness and typhoid was suspected. To arrive on the island it would have needed a carrier, but Steep Holm's 'navvies' included men from the Indian Army, a part of Asia where the disease was endemic. "One lad was very bad," Mr Parr said. "The weather was stormy at the time and the only boat that got through to us was a launch, which was for officers only. Another day went by before our motor barge arrived to take the sick man ashore.

"He died in the ambulance on his way to hospital in Barry. The well was investigated and found to contain typhoid bacteria. It had become polluted as the latrines had seeped through into it. This was not rectified while we were on the island, and all our water from then on came from the mainland in cans. It became as scarce as food and for washing we were rationed to one bowl for twelve men. If you were on cementwork and were at the end of the queue, it wasn't very successful. Towards the latter part of our stay they sent us some salt-water soap. That was like trying to get a lather from a pebble off the beach."

Other casualties were caused by accidents. Three men, newly posted to Major Bertlin's team, drowned off Flat Holm: "We very tragically lost three men when the Navy, at my request, attempted to land at Flat Holm. They were put into a dinghy with the idea that they should be rowed ashore.

"The dinghy collapsed and all three men were immediately drowned as they were encumbered by military equipment. The seaman rowing them, being without

The magazine of one of the island's 6-inch naval guns. The concrete and steel canopy of this 1941 emplacement protected it from air attack. Its gun stood to the left.

equipment, was saved. My officer, Hopper, awaiting them on the shore, was powerless to do anything to help."

On Steep Holm two sepoys of the Royal Indian Army Service Corps, in charge of a mule team, died on the island. Thomas Naughton, of 930 Port Construction Company, tells of German bombers dropping sea-mines into the Bristol Channel shipping lanes: "One sea-mine dropped on the island one night, before we had finished building the jetty. I was the only one hurt, with a brick and flying glass. We were playing cards by candlelight at the time, and I finished up in the RAF hospital near Barry. There were only twelve of us on the island then." S. G. Rock, too, remembers the mines: "My own recollection of the period was of frequent nightly visits of German aircraft, which mined the approaches to Cardiff and Barry, and of the floating mines which were daily swept and detonated around the island, causing the gulls to ascend in white clouds from Steep Holm. I also remember that our soldiers used to supplement their army rations with the fishy-tasting gulls' eggs collected from the cliffs."

For W. G. M. Jones as well, the gulls are remembered for their contribution to the war effort: "They seemed to appear on the same day towards the end of February. One day there was none—the next day the island was covered with them. They were laying all over the island during April and although one tried to preserve the greater part of Steep Holm as a bird sanctuary this was not at all popular with the men who reckoned to augment their low pay by selling the eggs. To have adopted a rigid attitude in the matter would have caused a great deal of ill-will. The men gathered the eggs and sold them to an NCO for one penny. He sold them to the man on the boat for twopence. He sold them to the shops in Barry for three-pence and the shopkeepers sold them for fourpence each. The eggs were palatable hard-boiled or fried. One man going down the cliff after eggs nearly lost his life in March 1943. I learned later that the rope had broken and there was great difficulty getting him up again. This happened near the searchlight at Rudder Rock."

G. A. King presents a summary of the state of the island's defences at the end of Major Bertlin's work: "The company of Royal Engineers laid a railway around the island for transporting stores and shells. They also built the iron jetty, and cut a three-tier trackway to the top of the island. A donkey engine was placed in a winch-house at the top of each one of these three cuts, to pull up the skips on railway lines. Gun emplacements were built at what we called the 'South' and 'Garden' ends of Steep Holm. We, that's myself and twelve other gunners of the Royal Artillery under a Battery Sergeant Major, put the six-inch coast defence guns in, and we also had two machine guns for air defence. There was also a troop of the Royal Indian Army Service Corps, with mules, under a King's Corporal."

The island's railway has a gauge of 60 cm (1 foot 11½ inches). Near each of the three winch-houses, there is a set of switch-over points. As with the older track from the South Landing, the rails and rusted sleepers of the east cliff railway are still largely in place. Major Bertlin's jetty was demolished at the end of the war, though his stone wall at the side of the beach—linking the jetty with the first railway incline—not only remains but looks set to stand for a thousand years. Two heavily clad copper cables, emerging from the shingle beach at the foot of the wall, carried a 20-line underwater telephone link to Flat Holm and Brean Down.

Concrete, reinforced with steel girders, was the basic building material for the 1940 fortifications. Searchlight posts were built above the sea at Calf Rock, South Landing, Rudder Rock and midway along the northern cliffs. This last post stands above a 90-foot sheer rock-face, linked to the top of the island by a contorted flight of 208 concrete steps following clefts in the cliff, and at one point taking to the air like a flying buttress on the side of a church.

The 6-inch gun emplacements are strung along the top of the island, on the edge of the scree slopes, and in three cases were built on the sites of Victorian batteries. Four main heavy gun emplacements, each 60 feet wide, are shielded with canopies of steel and concrete. A small pillbox, with shuttered slits at eye-level, stands above Rudder Rock and was the Battery Observation Post. There are two concrete blockhouses, which held diesel generators to power the island's four searchlights. The island's guns were percussion-fired and manually operated.

Four 6-inch BL Mark VII guns were issued by the Naval Armament Supply Office at Cardiff in autumn 1941 for the defence of the Steep Holm area. The island has four large, concrete 6-inch gun emplacements built by 930 Port Construction and Repair Company in the autumn of 1941—in pairs at Garden Battery and Summit Battery. However, possibly one half of each twin emplacement never had a gun. Two of the four 1941 guns used in "the Steep Holm area" were installed on Brean Down, though W. G. M. Jones assures us that when he arrived on the island in 1943 there were two fully operational batteries with two 6-inch guns each. By June 1945, all the Steep Holm guns had been removed, though the two were still at Brean Down. The origins of the four guns have been traced for us by historian

Searchlight post, reached by 208 steps, stands above the sheer northern cliffs. Its light stood guard over one of Britain's major convoy assembly and dispersal points.

N. J. M. Campbell of Ryde in the Isle of Wight. Gun number 1104 was made by the Royal Ordnance Factory, Woolwich, in 1901 and mounted in the battleship *Venerable*. In 1918 the gun was transferred to the armoured merchant cruiser *Edinburgh Castle*, and in 1939 to a similar ship, the *Ausonia*. Gun number 1783, manufactured by Armstrong Whitworth, was installed in the armoured cruiser *Donegal* in 1903, and went into store at Woolwich in 1918. Gun 1815, a Vickers product, was first in service at Devonport Gunnery School in 1903, and placed in the armoured merchant cruiser *Kildonan Castle* in 1916. Gun 2054, also by Vickers was in the battleship *Dominion* from 1904 to 1922. A story that Steep Holm had guns from the battleship *Royal Oak* is untrue. She was sunk in Scapa Flow at the beginning of the war and none of her twelve 6-inch guns was removed.

On the top of the island the Barracks were taken over as a mess and the over-spill was housed in a complex of Nissen huts to the west of the main block. Another concentration of concrete hut pads sprawls across the north-east corner of the island west of Tombstone Battery. In all they housed about 120 men. The iron debris on the ground includes rusting hoops and curved roofing sheets of corrugated iron.

North of the Priory ruin, at the head of the zig-zag railway, the ground is black with dust from the island's wartime coal dump. The Victorian Laboratory Battery became the island's sand pit.

A Scotsman, Bill Hunter of Kilmacolm in Renfrewshire, spent the summer of 1942 on Steep Holm as a 2nd lieutenant with a gun crew at Summit Battery. The island was serviced from Barry, 366 Heavy Coast Battery of the Royal Artillery operating all fixed gun positions in the upper Bristol Channel, including Barry, Brean Down, Cardiff, Flat Holm, Newport, Penarth, Portishead and Steep Holm. The main armament of 6-inch naval guns had an anti-ship role and practised on a large wooden target, the size of a motor boat, which was hauled by one of the regiment's support craft. Bill Hunter recalls: "On Steep Holm you had a great height and could appreciate the distance between the fall of shot. From 250 feet on the cliffs you are far more effective than firing at sea-level. You got on to the target quicker.

"Our function was coastal defence pure and simple. At Rudder Rock we had the Battery Observation Post. Below was one of the searchlights. These search-light points had to be near the water to give the maximum effect. If they were higher up they would have been more like a spotlight. From the bottom of the cliffs they could silhouette any boats and cover a wide area of sea. In fact we could light up the entire Channel. The enemy never came. They must have known how prepared we were."

Mr Hunter's Steep Holm summer ended when he was removed in the island's supply vessel, suffering acute sciatica, on a rough day. He then endured seasickness as well. Whilst he was stationed in the Bristol Channel, Bill Hunter arranged for the D'Oyly Carte opera company, on tour at Cardiff, to perform to the gunners on Flat Holm. Their operatic songs were interspersed with light-hearted skits parodying themselves. "The foghorn was going all the time this was happening," Mr Hunter remembers.

Some graffiti from the Second World War survive underground on Steep Holm in a Victorian gun battery. The northern of the two chambers at Rudder Rock has red-painted writing on one of its walls: "189 BTY, AA, GNRS W. COLLINS, T. BONNER, J. HEARSLEY, F. GREEN, W. DULY." Above, in the same paint, the letters "RIP" have been added as an afterthought. Below, in smaller black lettering, is a similar note: "RA, 11 December 1941, 189 COAST BATTERY, GNRS LAVER R.R., AVERY H.F., BISHOP G.S.W., FRANCE P." From these it is clear that 189 Coast Battery of the Royal Artillery was garrisoning Steep Holm in 1941. The letters "AA" stand for Anti-Aircraft. At least six anti-aircraft gun mountings are on the island. To be isolated on a rock, only five miles off Weston-super-Mare and yet without any contact with the civilian mainland, must have been an unappreciated posting.

A pencilling on a Barracks wall records one moment of light relief, a visit of a party from ENSA (acronym of the Entertainments National Service Association) on 31 October 1942. The names of the entertainers are autographed in the outline of

Top: Armoured doors, protecting part of the store of 6-inch naval shells at the rear of a wartime emplacement west of Garden Battery. Only the ammunition was contemporary. The guns themselves came from scrapped warships.
Bottom: Wartime generator house, near Summit Battery, provided power for the searchlights. It is a solidly-built concrete blockhouse, though the steel doors are rusting away.

Above: Rudder Rock, with the projecting roof of its searchlight canopy. "We could light up the whole channel," Bill Hunter remembers.
Opposite: The steps down to Rudder Rock searchlight post, built upwards from the bottom on a precarious foundation of stonework that is still sound. Only the guard rail has gone. The figure in the background is on the farthest western tip of the island.

a shell: "Fowler Bros, Isobel, Anne and Elsie." On one such trip the girls are said to have been stranded on the island by worsening weather, which was no doubt pleasurable for the battery's officers. W.G.M. Jones, serving on the island in 1943, remembers that one of the ENSA girls was Betty Hardcastle who lived in Weston-super-Mare.

Most of the reminiscing for this chapter was collected by Michael Yesson, the island's present engineer, as a result of an appeal for information about war-time Steep Holm printed by the Daily Mirror in 1976. Almost all the facts have been substantiated by cross-referencing, and the assembled material is vivid and alive. Yet no one has come forward to confirm the darker memories of Steep

Holm's war years held by many in Weston-super-Mare. Perhaps the mainland stories came about because Steep Holm and Flat Holm were forbidden territory, an active part of the country's front line in the Battle of the Atlantic. Little real information filtered back to Weston as the islands were serviced from the Welsh side of the Channel.

It is Weston folklore that the two islands were virtually Britain's joint Alcatraz. Locals, as they tell you about the islands, give history a certain timeless quality by referring to both Steep Holm and Flat Holm individually in the plural. That is the way their names were written on Victorian maps.

John Watts is the Weston boatman who runs the island ferry and he cherishes tales of the islands' past: "In the last war both islands, Steep Holms and Flat Holms, were used by the army. Flat Holms was an experimental place, especially for developing radar, because no one could hear or see what was happening. The place had 600 men and today most of the buildings are still there, vandalised, including rows of lavatories. German prisoners were also kept on Flat Holms— they were not the ordinary ones, but twelve desperate and dangerous Germans, and they were kept in barred cells. It's not the sort of place you can escape from, but one batch tried it on logs or something and were caught up the Channel at the English and Welsh Grounds Lightship. Another group, of two I think, also tried it, but were drowned. Some of these prisoners were taken over to Steep Holms for work parties."

Men of 930 Port Construction and Repair Company of the Royal Engineers pose outside Steep Holm Barracks, probably late in 1941. One of their Nissen huts can be seen in the distance, and the cameraman is leaning out of the window of another hut. Photograph taken by C. Maddison.

The arrival of Muntjac

Rodney Legg

RABBITS ARE the only mammals visitors are likely to see on Steep Holm. But intensive observation during the long summer of 1975 revealed two other island species, and deer were introduced to the island in 1977. There may be a Steep Holm vole, suggested tentatively as the short-tailed animal (*Microtus agrestis*) although it will need a captured individual before anything can be verified. The interest in this vole is that it led to the rediscovery of the fact that in 1897 the Orkney Vole (*Microtus arvalis*) was introduced to the island. No information exists of their fate. Trapping for small mammals in 1935 and 1974 was unsuccessful, but may have been carried out in the wrong parts of the island.

The other 1975 discovery was less questionable as the creature—a tiny hedgehog—was handled and can hardly have been mistaken for anything else. Its presence not only confirmed a longstanding claim that hedgehogs live on the island, but also proved successful breeding had taken place that year. It was no accidental introduction, as five other hedgehog sightings were reported in the following twelve months.

The occurrence of species such as these is in many ways less noteworthy than their absence. H. Tetley, writing about the island's mammals in 1938, was surprised not to find shrews, voles or mice on the island "which is all the more remarkable as there has been a fairly constant traffic to the island for many years, and one might have expected such animals to be introduced accidentally, for the island is only five miles from Weston-super-Mare and considerably less from Brean Down. If one compares Steep Holm with St. Kilda, which lies out in the North Atlantic about forty miles west of the outer Hebrides, one finds that although the latter is so isolated it possesses a field mouse (*Apodemus sylvaticus hirtensis*) and a house mouse (*Mus musculus muralis*) which have been so long established as to form new species. It is therefore very surprising to find such a complete absence on Steep Holm and no adequate reason can be advanced for it."

Both the St. Kilda animals are now regarded as no more than subspecies, at most, but this does not detract from the comparison.

Perhaps the greatest opportunities for animals to reach the island accidentally (or deliberately as smuggled pets) came with the 1860s fortification and the intensive wartime use in the 1940s. This could account for the arrival of voles and hedgehogs, and probably other small mammals which failed to find mates and could not establish themselves. Post-war natural history studies on the island have tended to ignore anything not a bird. Mammal records are sparse and no scientific work has been done, though the potential is more exciting than it looks. Bats have a home in one of the Steep Holm caves. Seals can hardly count as an island species, but they do visit the beach.

Rabbits are comparatively common on Steep Holm. This is the one mammal long associated with the island, and it was probably introduced by the mediaeval monks between 1160 and 1235. One of the earliest documented rabbit warrens in Norman England was on Brean Down. Promontories and islands provided an easy way of isolating the newly introduced animals and preventing their escaping. An added advantage was that islands were free from ground predators such as foxes, weasels, stoats and polecats. Ingenious methods were devised for catching the warrened rabbits, including circular stone-wall enclosures of prime sheltered grazing in Shetland—which were then blocked with a stone—and trap-doors in Norfolk, through which the animals dropped into a deep pit. Nothing has yet been found to show how Steep Holm's rabbits were trapped.

Elspeth M. Veale, in the *Agricultural Historical Review* for 1957, concludes that "the rabbit became established in the late 12th century on the small islands off the English coast". Later, in "the middle years of the 13th century coneygarths were being more widely set up on the mainland, but even late in the century rabbits were to be found only on certain estates". Rabbits were introduced to the Scillies before 1176 and to Lundy between 1183 and 1219. In 1492 they were thriving on Flat Holm. Skokholm also had a flourishing colony.

There were certainly rabbits established on Steep Holm by 1625, as there is a note in the account book of the Manor of Norton Beauchamp saying that because of the island's lack of grass, the island rabbits "be so fedd with garlicke, privet and elder (grasse lackeinge) that they do savor of the garlicke and privet in eating".

That observation, in terms of information value, almost exceeds anything studied about the rabbits in this most knowledgeable of centuries. W. G. M. Jones who was on the island in 1943, speaks of the "small reddish-brown rabbits" maintaining a "precarious existence".

In 1967 the population was estimated at 250 and there were several new warrens. Fifty-four rabbits were caught and marked (16 of them being captured twice). Five of the total were already tagged and had been trapped the previous year.

In 1975, though reduced by myxomatosis, the numbers were still relatively high. One night, whilst gull catching and ringing, the Cardiff University team led by Dr Peter Ferns counted nearly twenty rabbits. In daytime they remain within the dense shrub areas as animals that come into the open are vulnerable to attack from the gulls. Young rabbits have not learned this rule and are frequently found dead and mutilated beside the island paths in summer.

Top: Young rabbit. The stock was probably introduced by the monks in the 12th or early 13th century. They are distinctly more reddish than mainland rabbits.
Bottom: Stalk of Alexanders gnawed and toppled by rabbits. There is little grass on the island and the rabbits readily sample every other plant.

Evidence of rabbits is most noticeable in the island's densest cover, north-east of the Barracks. Here they often gnaw the lower stems of the Alexanders, sometimes toppling the plants. Some of the rabbits dig underground into the slope in this area, but others may live on the surface. Myxomatosis particularly attacks those living in burrows and the virus is thought to have reached the island in diseased fragments of dead rabbits brought by gulls from the mainland. Scientifically, the most interesting observation about the Steep Holm rabbits occurs in one of the oldest accounts. John Rutter writes in his *Delineations of the North-West Division of the County of Somerset* in 1829: "A few rabbits continue to exist on the rock, whose fur is of a redder cast than rabbits usually have." Here is a general topographical writer, thirty years before Wallace and Darwin, noticing that colonies of animals isolated from the mainstream of their kind tend to develop different characteristics. He did not express it that way but he recorded the relevant fact. Today the Steep Holm rabbits are still noticeably different from those on the mainland, although some new stock could have been introduced from Somerset if the native Steep Holm colony was over-cropped. The mediaeval type may have partially assimilated back to the norm, but the typical island rabbit still has some red markings.

J. W. Hunt, who visited Steep Holm in about 1955, recalls that the rabbits were "red behind the ears, like the Belgian hare". On 23 August 1975, Robert Spiller, a Royal Marine from Deal who has spent a considerable time on the island, saw the same coloration on a rabbit near Tombstone Battery. This characteristic (usually orange) fur on the back of the neck, is now noticed in most of the rabbits seen on Steep Holm. It is probably a case of visitors being aware and looking out for the markings, rather than the colony becoming more distinctive. As for the single vole sighting, there are no historical accounts of small mammals on Steep Holm but in May 1975 a visiting naturalist, Tony Phelps from Swanage, saw a vole as he walked across the island. He thought it was a Short-tailed Vole but could not be definite about the species as he had only glimpsed the animal escaping into Alexanders.

The importance of the Orkney Vole is that it is a distinct relict species, once occurring all over Britain and now in its last stronghold. Introductions apart, it was even possible Steep Holm might have had its own species—and the island shares with its Scottish counterparts a Norse connection. The "Viking mice" of the Hebrides were introduced by the longships.

Unfortunately a difficulty in investigating apparent small mammal holes on Steep Holm is that they invariably turn out to be caused by the decayed stumps of Alexanders. On the other hand Skomer, on the south Wales coast, has a distinct sub-species of Bank Vole (*Clethrionomys glareolns skomerensis*).

Hedgehogs are a more positive matter as a number have been sighted. John Barratt, a Bristol member of the old island trust, said in 1973 that he thought there were hedgehogs on Steep Holm. Confirmation of this came after dark on 31 July 1975. A worker from International Voluntary Service opened the Barracks door to find "a baby hedgehog just outside". Other members of the team came to look and John Cockings, the group leader, said the animal was definitely very young and small. The following week John Cockings saw a young hedgehog, possibly the same one, crossing the path between the Barracks and Split Rock Battery. The only possible hedgehog traces noticed previously were snail shells eaten out from the back, a common hedgehog habit, but it then seemed equally likely that gulls had learnt the same method. An adult hedgehog with baby were also found outside the Barracks in August 1976, and a dead baby at Summit Battery in September. Both Tony Parsons and the Poole Friends of the Earth group, at different times in 1976, took night photographs of hedgehogs near the Barracks. Parsons, a veterinary surgeon, examined his animal and reported it fat and healthy. Like all warm-blooded life on Steep Holm (including humans) it carried harvest mites, but Parsons was surprised to find no trace of the hedgehog flea (*Archaeopsylla erinacei*). In April 1976 Tony Parsons found an adult male hedgehog dead, only a few yards away from the spot where he had taken photographs. Its misadventure had been to jam its head into a can of dried milk. Another hedgehog, a young adult not more than two years old, was found dead on the path at Garden Battery in June 1977. At the beginning of the following month, a Forest School Camp held on the island brought reports of three adult hedgehogs—alive and well. The first, at 9.30 pm on the 5th, was to the east of the Barracks. The next evening, at 11.00 pm, there was one at Garden Battery. On the 8th, at 10.15 pm, another hedgehog was midway between Garden Battery and the Barracks: "It was snuffling about in scrub, and completely unconcerned at having three observers. It didn't curl up or object to being photographed." These records reflect the distribution of observers, rather than the hedgehogs, in being confined to the southern scrub. It should be pointed out that little human activity takes place on the north side of the island after dark.

Perhaps the clue to the presence of hedgehogs is contained in Richard Fitter's *The Ark in our Midst*, published in 1959. There were no hedgehogs in the Scottish islands at the turn of the century: "Surprising as it may seem, those who dwell in hedgehogless country seem to yearn for hedgehogs. Mull, for instance, is supposed to have been populated by the descendants of hedgehogs brought home as pets by men who went to Territorial camps in the south." The Steep Holm hedgehogs may be the result of recent introductions, as six animals are said to have been released beside Garden Cottage in May 1975. The specimens (four males and two females) had been picked up on main roads in north Dorset. Their journey to Steep Holm was regarded as rescue. One estimate of the Steep Holm hedgehog population, calculated from the frequency at which droppings are found, is a pair per third of an acre of suitable habitat—giving a total of about 200 animals for the island as a whole. A figure such as this is not inconsistent with recent introductions. Perhaps 500 animals is the optimum, giving one of the highest densities of hedgehogs for anywhere in Europe.

As a shrubby piece of land, with acres of tangled undergrowth, Steep Holm is perfect hedgehog country. Where the animal might seem to have problems, though, is in finding sufficient moisture—for in drought there is no surface water anywhere on the island and worms and snails also become scarce. But hedgehogs have survived. Even if they only arrived in 1975, they have still managed to breed and come through two of the worst droughts of any century. Insects generally remain plentiful and provide not only food but a substitute for drink. Their insect eating was verified on 9 July 1977, at the end of a hot spell, by the discovery of some droppings in an area of privet scrub. These hedgehog faeces contained two woodlice (almost certainly *Armadillidium vulgare*), a centipede (*Lithobius forficatus*) and a ground beetle (*Abax parallelepipedus*) as well as a tiny piece of moss (probably *Hypnum cupressiforme*) and several small leaves of grass (probably *Festuca ovina*). The vegetation was probably eaten deliberately (rather than swallowed along with an item of prey) as the strands of grass were more than half an inch. A larger dropping, found at South Landing, consisted entirely of the remains of earwigs (*Forficula auricularia*) the number of pincers present showing at least 22 of the insects had been eaten. Perhaps future study may show the extent to which their diet is supplemented by gull eggs and young chicks when these are in season.

Hans Kruuk, studying the Ravenglass dunes in 1962, found that hedgehogs eat gull fledglings. Their attack is to seize the nearest part of the bird and immobilise it by climbing on top. The hedgehog starts eating the bird's rear end taking the preen-gland and sometimes the entrails as well.

Hedgehogs will also leap at slow-worms they come across, but mostly the slow-worm exposes itself in the daytime, and the hedgehog hunts at night. Slow-worms have an almost passive style of living, and spend most of their time in burrows, under stones, or beneath corrugated iron. They tend to be locally abundant, and many of the mainland gardens where they thrive also have hedgehogs. However, ecologies of change are bitterly resented by some old-school purists who see altering circumstances as a threat to their prejudices. A request was made in 1977 for the "eradication" of the island hedgehogs, though fortunately not by a Trust member, and shows that attitudes Kenneth Allsop spent his life attacking are still alive. Ken's book *In the Country* contains the story of a near-drowned hedgehog and the happy ending when it was reborn in the airing cupboard. May the members of the Trust that carries his name never commission the persecution of wildlife.

Bats, whose species is not recorded, used to be resident in Jubilee Cave. This cave is near sea-level, in the north-east corner of the island. Writing on the cave wall gives 1935 as its discovery date, though it was probably known earlier. It penetrates about sixty feet into the island and is reached by crossing a tidal rock pool.

It was common knowledge to the cavers, however, and in about 1969 they described Jubilee "teeming with bats, banging and flying everywhere". By 1975 the position was far less healthy and only one small dung heap, and no bat, was seen. Bat numbers have declined over most of the country in that period, but reductions on the Steep Holm scale are exceptional. Bats are occasionally observed flying near the Barracks, but some at least may have flown across from the mainland. A young male Pipistrelle (*Pipistrellus pipistrellus*) was netted behind the Barracks in September 1977.

The other mammals in the visitor category are the occasional grey seals (*Halichoerus grypus*) that stray upstream in midsummer from their Welsh breeding grounds. An animal sometimes stays on the southern side of Steep Holm for several days but in rougher weather the shore has little shelter. The island is at the upstream limit of their distribution in the Bristol Channel.

Opposite: Bats used to be found in Jubilee Cave, but their most likely haunt now is here in Five Johns Cave, towards the top-right at the back—high above the tide line and beyond the reach of explorers.

To "enhance" Steep Holm is one of the Trust's foremost objectives and I was delighted when we were offered the chance to enrich the island's rather limited wildlife in 1977. Dr Oliver Dansie, who was Kenneth Allsop's physician in Hertford-shire, generously donated the Trust a pair of Muntjac deer (*Muntiacus reevesi*).

The animals were rescued from a wood where they were due to be shot. Dr Dansie is the country's leading expert on this species of deer. The catch-up was approved by the Nature Conservancy and the British Deer Society, but the circum-stances allowed no time for consultation within the Trust, and the question of the animals' suitability and fate became entirely my responsibility. Peter Carne, the editor of the magazine *Deer*, called them "an intriguing addition indeed to the island's fauna".

They are tiny animals, not much larger than a fox, and are a living fossil. Though the present Muntjac wild in England and Wales are the successors of animals brought from China, that escaped from deer parks, there were almost identical animals in Europe 35 million years ago. They are the only surviving representative of an enormous group of extinct mammals, the Palaeomerycidae. Dr Dansie points out that Muntjac were old when other deer were "sharing ancestors with the giraffe".

Their size and habitat make them right for Steep Holm. Whereas most deer are happy with a field of long grass, or a farmer's corn, these are not grazing animals. They are exclusively a browsing deer and spend almost all their time in dense scrub, "an empty ecological niche," as Dansie puts it. The island at present has 17 acres of scrub and its area has expanded from a mere six acres in 1950. Nothing has yet held this trend in check.

Visually, they are also right for the island, as they are pocket-size deer blending immediately into the background, and moving around as individuals rather than herds. Their presence on Steep Holm equates with the use by the Normans of islands as naturally contained enclosures for their rabbits. "I have only moved deer that would otherwise be eliminated by shotgun drives," Dr Dansie explains. "But never to places where they might escape and become a problem, albeit an imagin-ary one."

From the scientific viewpoint, the Steep Holm experiment may be revealing and provide data about the animals' life and habits. This is important as Muntjac is potentially, on present evidence, the most adaptable foreign deer ever to escape into the British countryside. Since a few broke out of parks at Woburn Abbey and Whipsnade in the 1940s the species has established substantial numbers in the south Midlands and westwards to Wales, but its notable achievement is the capacity to thrive in patches of farmland abandoned for ultimate development beside the fringes of London and the new towns of Hertfordshire.

Dr Dansie says: "Many people like to see Muntjac about and it is the large neglected garden that maintains the population in the towns. With their base secure they can wander the streets, grazing the verges, pruning the roses, and gather-ing acorns under the remaining mature oaks."

In a century it is likely the Muntjac will be known to the suburban inhabitants of every town in England and Wales, though usually as a result of the inevitable road casualties that are the penalty for a species adapting into man's unintended town-edge wildernesses.

Pointers for further research were set out by the Mammal Society of the British Isles in 1959: "Study the acclimatisation of Muntjac. There is some evidence that mortality during hard winters is selective. Are the winter breeding strains being eliminated?" On the island, with its milder winters, the original all-year breeding genes are unlikely to be impaired, though there is no proof this is happening on the mainland anyway.

Jim Taylor Page, compiling the *Field Guide to British Deer*, produced page charts of the seasonal behaviour of each species, except Muntjac. In its place he wrote: "Little is known of the seasonal behaviour of Muntjac in Great Britain. This page is left blank and it is hoped that you will assist in filling it in."

The advantage an island offers for study is a detached and simplified environment. Attention is focused on details that would be difficult to isolate on the mainland. It is difficult to explain quite the significance some trivial event can have on an island, and the excitement it brings to those working there, though explorers Buxton and Hopkins' story of the arrival of the human flea on a Pacific island does illustrate the curiosity that is the pre-requisite for all research: "The placid natives of Aitutaki, observing that the little creatures were constantly restless and inquisitive, and even at times irritating, drew the reasonable inference that they were the souls of deceased white men."

On summertime trips we hope to be able to show off the island's strange deer to visitors, though as they are few and secretive this cannot be taken as a guarantee.

Muntjac doe takes her first look at Steep Holm. She had spent 22 hours in this crate, carried by truck from Hertfordshire and then by boat from Weston. Yet she stepped calmly onto the island and watched coolly as her 'captors' took photographs.

These deer leave few traces of their presence and movement, noticeable paths through the undergrowth only occurring on Steep Holm in early summer in the great tracts of quick-growing, fleshy Alexanders. Slots are only likely to be found in damp soil. Droppings are added regularly to small heaps, often in impenetrable thickets. These unobtrusive qualities are the key to the Muntjac's 20th century English acceptibility, in contrast to the treatment of gregarious species. As Dansie says: "There is no herding or flocking animal whose numbers have not suffered. Is this, perhaps, because man is the supreme visual hunter and as soon as any animal is out of sight it is out of mind. Environment has changed quicker than evolution, and it so happens the Muntjac have also stepped into an empty niche in man's empty and idle mind." You are probably more likely to see them on television as they are proving very popular with the media. One en-route for Cotswold Wildlife Park featured on the BBC local news from Bristol on 2 March 1977.

Although the Muntjac were released on the island early in 1977, and despite several hundred people visiting the island including some who tramped the undergrowth looking for them, none was seen until 5 July. Then, at 10.00 pm, Howell Jones disturbed a 9-inch high mammal "of indeterminate colour" on an old Nissen hut footing north-west of the Barracks: "It disappeared up the path at very high speed." The following night, at 10.55 pm, Amy Pluim-Mentz saw "a hind leg disappearing into bushes" between Garden Battery and the Barracks. Stan Rendell, on Saturday 23 July at 9.30 pm, met a Muntjac on an overgrown path near a waterhole: "I suddenly saw this brown animal right in front of me. It disappeared into the bushes straight away. I think it had just gone down to get a drink." A few days later at two o'clock one afternoon, a Muntjac burst a hole two feet wide through one of the nets Tony Parsons was using to catch birds. They seem to have bred, as sets of tiny tracks have been found running alongside normal sized ones.

There is further potential for the enrichment of life on Steep Holm. The islands of Eigg, Islay, Muck and Gigha have their own forms of short-tailed vole, each judged to be a sub-species, and the controlled release of the mainland type of this harmless small mammal, to Steep Holm, would provide facilities for the study of the evolution of physical differences—in the longest term imaginable, not stretching into the next decade, but for a thousand years. They would act as a comparison population for those engaged in the understanding of the various relict and introduced species of the Scottish islands that are loosely termed the "Viking mice". Actively encouraging the takeover by nature of a habitat abandoned by man, to allow it to reach its optimum wilderness potential, was a constant theme in Kenneth Allsop's writings and he totally rejected styles of nature reserve management that imposed conformity and status quo. It is offshore, however, where the island is always liable to produce its biggest surprises. The five foot high erect, pointed back-fin of an adult male Killer Whale (*Orcinus orca*) emerged from a bank of mist on the morning of 17 April 1976. It appeared on the starboard side of a small blue boat packed with day trippers, which had overshot the island in a fog. The animal, which must have been 25 feet long, was in the deep-water shipping lane about a mile north-west of Rudder Rock. On that same trip, the island's ferry also had close encounters with the *Balmoral* steamer and a large tanker, being tossed in their wakes. "It was like a Conrad novel," Colin Graham remembers.

Blue slow-worms

Rodney Legg

THE DISTINCTIVE fact about many of the Steep Holm reptiles, its slow-worms, is that they are bluish. Most adults are covered with blue spots, across the upper parts of their bodies, and particularly on the dorso-lateral series between the demarcation line between the light colour of the back and the heavier (though often bluish-black) markings of the underparts. This coloration is not apparent in young slow-worms but begins to appear during the third year of their lives.

Slow-worms are the only Steep Holm reptile (*Anguis fragilis*) and the author of the Collins' book on *The British Amphibians and Reptiles*, Malcolm Smith, claims the blueness only occurs in males. Far from only being recorded in Steep Holm slow-worms, it was first described by A. de Demidoff in 1840 for the eastern shore of the Russian Black Sea at Port Euxin. The blue strain on Steep Holm continues into the 1970s, with examples up to sixteen inches in length, and more bluish than grey, being seen in both 1976 and 1977.

It is difficult to estimate quite how common the slow-worm is on Steep Holm. Generally, through the summer, animals are reported every fortnight, and sometimes the claims are astounding, like the International Voluntary Service team in 1975 who, even under persistent questioning, refused to withdraw the statement that they had found an animal a metre in length. It would be the longest slow-worm ever discovered outside continental Russia, and whatever its true size, has entered island folklore. In most other cases, gulls have grabbed the animal's tail, showing that many more must have been gobbled head first.

The dependable way of finding Steep Holm slow-worms is to lift rusting pieces of Second World War ironwork but though this can often provide a couple of examples it also disturbs the very habitat on which they depend for survival. It is impossible to replace corrugated iron precisely as it was found, or to be completely sure you are not tramping across other slow-worms, or that your disturbance is not about to scatter young animals.

Slow-worms occur on Lewis and other islands in the Outer Hebrides, as they do on the Shetland Islands and, off Wales, Anglesey, Bardsey and Flat Holm. They are absent from Ireland, from which they must have been eliminated by the last ice-age, though there is every reason to think that reintroductions would do well. Returning to the Steep Holm blueness, Malcolm Smith observes that such colour may "vary from light Cambridge blue to deep ultramarine". The general Steep Holm colour seems to be the former, an overall mild sky-blue, and it is only through the observation of marked or captive animals that we will know whether his secondary observation–that "the colour is not constant; the blue may disappear at any time, leaving a brown spot in its place"–applies on the island. One bluish specimen, eighteen inches long but with only a stumpy tail, was found by Tony Phelps in 1975, who was working at the time on reptiles for the Nature Conservancy at Furzebrook in Dorset. He estimated it was between sixty and seventy years old.

Slow-worms have been recorded on Steep Holm for many decades, their distribution in recent years ranging from dense scrub at the centre of the island to batteries on the cliff edge and youngsters beside the ruins of the inn but isolated, older reports that the island has adders and common lizards have never been substantiated. Wall lizards might seem a more appropriate reptile for the island's geography and climate.

An 18-inch slow-worm, medium sized by Steep Holm standards, though it would have been longer if it had not suffered tail damage. Most have been seized at some stage or another by a gull.

Birds and birdwatching

Tony Parsons

CONSIDERING THE past absence of consistent observation, Steep Holm has a long bird species list and some notable sightings. There is no shortage of passage birds, and the regular visiting and field-work that has taken place since the Kenneth Allsop Memorial Trust bought the island has resulted in a sharp rise in new records. In 1976 Steep Holm was registered as a ringing centre by the British Trust for Ornithology, its 1977 tally totalling 462 birds and including a Nightjar.

The birds can be divided roughly into two groups. Firstly, the regular breeding species, and secondly, the passage birds and irregular breeders.

Among the regular breeders, the most obvious to anyone arriving in spring and summer is the Herring Gull. The Steep Holm gull colony contains three species, but the Herring Gull dominates the scene. This was the colony chosen by Maurice Tibbles for his film *The Private Life of the Herring Gull.* They nest in every available space from the jetty to the Ordnance Survey's instrument point, from inside old ammunition bunkers to the middle of the main path. Records of Great Black-backed Gulls breeding on Steep Holm date back to Colonel George Montagu, who was told of their presence by Welsh fishermen ("who call them Cobbs") probably prior to 1808. Cecil Smith, in his *Birds of Somersetshire,* (1869), said the Great Black-backed Gull colony had troubles at that time: "Although they used to breed on Steep Holmes *(sic),* I believe they do so no longer, as that little island is almost destroyed as a breeding station by Government fortification works and Bristol and Cardiff excursionists."

In 1832, Reverend John Skinner saw what were apparently Herring Gulls breeding, but the first record of Lesser Black-backed Gulls does not appear until 1901. Then ten to twelve pairs each of Herring and Lesser Black-backed Gull were noted by the Reverend Francis Linley Blathwayt. In 1907 he returned and noted of the Herring Gull: "Numbers have I think increased of late. I saw quite 25 pairs of adults about the island." The rise continued, and in 1917 Dr. J. Wiglesworth counted a total of 120 pairs of Herring Gull and 35 pairs of Lesser Black-backed Gull. By the

The return of the Peregrine falcons is shown dramatically by their leavings, in terms of the corpses of gulls and pigeons. The predators seize their prey in flight and then land briefly to tear the guts out. Smaller targets are demolished entirely.

1930s there were over 1000 pairs altogether; in 1969 Operation Seafarer recorded 3,550 Herring Gull and more than 600 Lesser Black-backed Gull nests. In the mid-1970s there were around 6,500 pairs of Herring Gulls and more than 500 pairs of Lesser Black-backed. Herring Gull numbers now seem to have stabilised and there is no longer any real fear that Steep Holm's gull population will reach the record 15,000 to 17,500 pair levels of Walney Island, Morecambe Bay, the Isle of Man, Fife, or Puffin Isle, Anglesey. The Great Black-backed Gull was not officially proved to breed on Steep Holm until 1923, but had probably been present for a few seasons. Nowadays, between 30 and 50 pairs would be a reasonable estimate for most years, although 86 nests were found in 1962.

Anyone visiting the island in summer might be excused for assuming that the wholesale slaughter of 19th century seabirds was being re-enacted. The island is littered with the carcases of gulls, from tiny nestlings to adults. The reasons for the high death rate are numerous, but not least among them is a natural 'falling by the wayside' which, in a summer population of some 30,000 adult birds and nestlings is bound to be noticeable. The physical factors of population pressure, summer heat and distance from food supplies all take their toll.

It is now certain that no single terrible disease or poisoning is responsible for the annual mortality. Post-mortem examination of some birds shows the expected cases of aspergillosis (a fungal disease), bacterial infections, egg-peritonitis and other pathological conditions, as well as the frequent 'battered baby' syndrome, where nestlings straying from their parents' territory are immediately and viciously set upon by other adults, usually with instantly fatal results. Hugh Boyd, in 1963, estimated that more than half of each year's 12,000 or so nestlings died before fledging.

Dr Peter Ferns of Cardiff University reported a far greater failure rate in 1975. He considered the average for a normal year would be 0.9 to one immature bird per nest, which is in itself lower than Boyd's 1.5. Yet the year's survey showed nothing approaching either sets of statistics: "Though the breeding population, 6,000 to 7,000 pairs, was no smaller in 1975 than 1974, breeding success in 1975 was low, the average number of chicks raised to fledging per breeding pair of adults being 0.64. The average clutch size in 1975 was only two eggs."

The Lesser Black-backed Gull prefers to nest in the more open areas, whereas the Herring Gull prefers the rocky slopes and ledges. As the 'urbanisation' of the colony progresses, living standards deteriorate, and in the 1960s some Lesser Black-backs started to nest in trees. One hardly expects to find a gull's nest six feet up in an elder, but the sight has become an annual one on Steep Holm. The Great Black-backs keep right out of the way, nesting on the crags and ledges in the less accessible parts of the island but, nevertheless, they enter the statistics of mortality in a small way.

The one other seabird that now breeds is the Cormorant. The first official record of breeding is in 1934, when some ten pairs were present, but Harry Cox knew of them for some years prior to this and it is likely that they were already breeding in 1901, when young birds were noted. "It is the sole breeding place in the county of the Cormorant," wrote Dr. J. Wiglesworth of Winscombe, who had rowed around the island several times, in 1917. He frequently asked the islanders to look out for unusual birds. Thomas Grills, who was "H.M. Coastguard, Steep-

A Great Black-back gull lifts off from the cliff. These massive birds have a wingspan of more than five feet and nest on exposed crags.

holme Island", wrote to the doctor on 23 July 1918 that the current season had not been successful: "I am quite positive the Cormorants did not nest on the island this year. I kept all the north side of the island under close observation up to the present and there has been no sign of any young birds, the old birds have been here off and on apparently for feeding or passing in the direction of Breandown, some-times the pair, at other times singly." The colony, on the north cliffs, had crept up to between 15 and 20 pairs by the late thirties and has been relatively stable ever since, with a slight increase to the present level of about 45 nests each year. The island has the Bristol Channel's principal Cormorant cliffs. Cormorants can be frequently seen on their flights to and from the inland reservoirs where they feed. The greatest disturbance they endure on the island comes not from visitors—none of the island's paths is visible from any of the nests—but when the *Balmoral* steamer passes close inshore and almost scrapes the cliff between Summit Battery and Rudder Rock. Her passengers then see every Cormorant on Steep Holm, and up to 65 birds have been counted flying out from the lower cliffs.

Another bird of the coastal cliffs is the Rock Pipit. It is likely that Rock Pipits have bred on Steep Holm throughout the present century and probably long before-hand. Between one and five pairs nest each year, but sightings are infrequent unless the effort is made to find them by walking the undercliff scree—although in the past they have bred in the Barracks wall.

The Stock Dove is present, too, on the cliffs and likes to nest as near to the sea as it reasonably can without suffering inundation from storm-spray. Its main strong-holds are on the north-east corner and the central southern part of the island. Nest

Steep Holm is "the sole breeding place in the county of the Cormorant," Dr. J. Wiglesworth noted in 1917. They nest, unperturbed, side by side with the Herring Gulls.

sites are natural holes in the cliff, or artificial ones in the ruined inn. They even nest well up inside Reservoir Cavity above the tide-line to the west of the South Landing. Probably three to six pairs nest on the island annually.

It is difficult to know how long Wood Pigeons have been breeding on the island, but they must have been present for some years before the first nests were found. Nowadays two or three pairs nest, usually very close to the ground in the elders.

H M Coast Guard
Steepholme Island
25th July 1918

Dear Sir

In reply to your letter of the 18th re the Cormorants, I am quite positive the Cormorants did not nest on the Island this year I kept all the north side of the Island under close observation up to the present + there has been no sign of any young birds, the old birds have been here off + on apparently for feeding or passing in the direction of Breandown, sometimes the pair at other times singly.

The Peregrine Falcon hatched out four young birds. The Whealear that I mentioned to you disappeared early in June. I am afraid the Manx Shearwater does not nest here. as I have never heard it; no other birds noted only the usual residents. I will write to you later if I see any strangers when they migrate

Yours faithfully
Thos Grills

Island coastguard Thomas Grills writes about the status of the Cormorant and Peregrine to Dr. J. Wiglesworth during the First World War.

While on the subject of pigeons and doves, the feral pigeon should be mentioned. Small flocks of racing pigeons are a frequent sight around the island, but most of their visits are purely transitory. Sometimes an exhausted or lost bird stays for a while and dead ones are found occasionally around the barracks. It is noticeable from their rings that most are 'first-year' birds and, once lost or delayed, their owners write them off and are not interested in knowing more—which is probably just as well since some of them supplement the diet of visiting Peregrines. Most experienced observers believe that the Rock Dove in its true wild form does not occur on Steep Holm, and probably never has occurred.

Both the Shelduck and the Oystercatcher are frequent visitors to the island. Several pairs of Shelduck spend the summer on and by the island, but breeding is restricted to a very small number of nests, and is probably irregular nowadays. This may be compared with the situation around 1920, when 40 to 50 pairs of Shelduck nested in the rocks, on the cliffs and in the dense vegetation, as well as in rabbit burrows. This level of Shelduck nests on a small island is hardly compatible with the presence of several thousand gulls, but there is no reason why a small number of pairs should not continue to breed successfully. Oystercatchers have bred, and have possibly been irregular breeders for a number of years. Certainly there is no recent proof of breeding, but one or two often fly over from the mainland to feed at low tide.

The breeding passerines consist of a selection of common garden birds, but even these take on a new interest in their island home. Opportunities arise for the study of virtually closed populations, as Ray Poulding's work on the Dunnock in the 1960s shows. Dunnocks are a common and successful breeding species, with at least 40 pairs, but not without their problems. The lack of surface water has resulted in more than one falling into the underground reservoir in summer, and others drowning in buckets, though a water-pan constructed in 1976 is bringing some relief. Every Dunnock (and most of the resident thrushes) handled in late summer is infested with harvest mite larvae—up to 500 on a single bird.

Even announcing one's territory in the face of a cacophony of gulls must be trying for the smaller species. Some thirty pairs of Blackbirds and five or so pairs of Song Thrushes form Steep Holm's normal complement, but Song Thrushes in particular can suffer severely in hard weather, as in the winter of 1916-17, when they were temporarily exterminated on the island. The numbers of Blackbirds and Song Thrushes are augmented in autumn by some immigrants, which are probably mainly short-distance travellers in dispersal and feeding movements.

The Robin has certainly bred since before the First World War, and probably on a regular basis. Although they can be remarkably difficult to detect in spring, they become very apparent in autumn and probably about five to ten pairs breed annually. The Wren is usually a sedentary species and will undoubtedly repay studying in detail. Some observers have claimed plumage variations in comparison with mainland birds, but much work would be necessary to determine any consistent variation and it is unlikely that a distinctive 'Steep Holm Wren' is ever going to arise. In favourable conditions, Wren populations can rise remarkably quickly and it seems likely that the 1976 post-breeding population of well over a hundred individuals is the highest ever recorded.

Top: A Steep Holm Dunnock. The island has a resident population of about 40 pairs. Work carried out on them in 1963, by Ray Poulding, revealed a possible method for ageing this species by its iris colour.
Bottom: A brood of Peregrine falcons pictured in their Steep Holm eyrie in May 1936 by Harry Cox. The Peregrine is again a frequent island sight and its return as a breeding species is imminent.

Many other species breed or have bred on an irregular basis and odd pairs of numerous species are to be expected at intervals. Greenfinches, Linnets, Carrion Crows, Jackdaws and Starlings are all more or less regular, and other species noted as having bred in the past are recorded in the list at the end of the chapter. Variations in breeding levels of some species are bound to occur with variations in the vegetation. Meadow Pipits and Skylarks, both breeding in the past, would have difficulty in finding any usable area for nesting nowadays.

We now come to two of the most important species on the island's list, the Raven and the Peregrine Falcon. Indeed, whereas the smaller species were often considered too insignificant or too generally common to record, one can find a multitude of breeding records for both species for the first four decades of this century. Whenever anyone wrote about the island's birds, they included the Peregrine, and coastguard Thomas Grills in his report about the Cormorants on 25 July 1918 adds: "The Peregrine Falcon hatched out four young birds." The Peregrine has not been a proven breeder on the island since the war, or the Raven since 1971, although both are still frequent visitors outside the breeding season.

The two species do breed within easy flying distance of Steep Holm and plans are already in hand for protection should either species honour the island again in the future. The main eyrie used by the Peregrines was not far from military quarters, though well down the cliffs. It was official policy during the last war to kill Peregrines to prevent them taking carrier pigeons. The Ravens, on the other hand, used at least three alternative sites in different years, are unlikely to have suffered so much from human disturbance and, anyway, were still present long after the war. Increasing numbers of gulls are unlikely to have been a deterrent, as the Carrion Crow still breeds in the face of such opposition. After the war Peregrine numbers increased dramatically until 1955, and went into a major decline from 1958 onwards as a result of chlorinated hydro-carbons. Ravens suffered severe reductions too and Steep Holm was soon affected. Regular Peregrine breeding now takes place within 15 miles of the island and there is every chance, once the pesticide menace has been eliminated, that they will return. Ravens are also likely to recolonise the island as they have bred on Brean Down almost every year since at least the 1890s, withstanding far more disturbance from visitors than occurs on Steep Holm. Their numbers on the western uplands are now very high, a flock of 107 Ravens being counted on Exmoor in autumn 1975.

Despite the absence of irrefutable evidence of breeding it is quite certain that the Razorbill, Guillemot and Puffin all bred on Steep Holm in the 19th century. The appearance of unrelated notes to this effect at various times during the 1800s and early 1900s indicates that the island must have held numbers of all these auks. In 1858, Hayward noted that the Guillemot was present in considerable numbers, being more common than the Razorbill, and that the Puffin, too, was there. Earlier in 1829, John Rutter in his *Delineations of the north-western division of the County of Somerset* referred to the "vast numbers" of seabirds there, without being more specific, but it is likely that at least some of the eggs collected on the island and sent to the sugar refineries in Bristol would have been those of the auks. References to Kittiwakes are somewhat more vague, but the probability is that W. D. Crotch was right including it in his 1850 *List of Birds' Eggs* found in Somersetshire.

The latest record of any of these species breeding on the island appears in James Turner's notes for 1912. Turner, as recorder for the Somerset Archaeological and Natural History Society, received information from the tenant, James Sleeman, that the Puffin definitely bred there in 1912. No mention was made of the other auks, although Laurence Whish reported having examined "a few eggs" of Guillemots breeding on Brean Down in the same year. The turbid waters around Steep Holm could never have presented optimum opportunities for auks and in the face of reducing populations nationally it might seem inevitable they would disappear from the island. On the other hand this cannot be the whole story as Puffins were gone from Steep Holm by the turn of the century but there were still 3,500 pairs on Lundy in 1939.

Turner was assured in 1912 that the Manx Shearwater bred regularly on Steep Holm. As with Puffins, they would have nested in disused rabbit burrows, or dug their own. The nocturnal habits of this bird would mean that day visitors would be unlikely to report it and this might account for the lack of any confirmatory record. Shearwaters breed on Lundy and Skokholm and are frequently sighted off the island, often moving up the Bristol Channel in front of a spell of rough weather.

Turning from the breeding species to the passage birds, one encounters one of the most interesting aspects of Steep Holm's biology. Migration is an immensely wide-ranging subject, and can be said to be occurring to some extent throughout the year. As the last northward-bound Swifts pass through late in June, they may well overlap with the first southward-bound Common Sandpipers, for example.

Passage becomes most noticeable in two main phases. The spring migration northwards from April to June is generally not of a spectacular nature and is often difficult to assess in the clamorous, tumultuous environment of a large gull colony. But studying southward movements in autumn can be much more rewarding. The gulls have virtually deserted the island for the mainland by the time the main passage commences in August, and the migrants' numbers are at this time augmented by large numbers of juvenile birds. Movements of birds in autumn are orientated mainly from north-west to south-east at this point, from the Welsh coast across Flat Holm and Steep Holm to the Somerset coast.

Indeed, on some occasions, when a favourable weather pattern prevails, a very large percentage of the migrants passing out of Wales uses this route. Some of the migrants move primarily by day, such as the finches, larks, pipits and hirundines (swallows and martins). Others, tending to move by night, include the warblers, chats and thrushes.

A clear night with light winds will start a movement that may be 'grounded' on Steep Holm by an autumn mist later in the night. In these conditions, the next morning may show every patch of scrub holding its quota of nocturnal immigrants. A clear, still morning in October will bring huge flocks of diurnal migrants. A few will use this mid-Channel 'service-station' for a temporary stay, but most of them will pass on without stopping.

Many species are well represented in these movements. Phylloscopus and Sylvia warblers, and an occasional Acrocephalus warbler, are encountered throughout August and September, and into October. The dominant Phylloscopus in August is the Willow Warbler, whose numbers diminish as September advances, to give way to the Chiffchaff. Blackcaps, Garden Warblers, Whitethroats and Lesser Whitethroats all pass through in small to moderate numbers, but are often unnoticed until caught for ringing. The occasional Sedge and Reed Warblers find little comfort in Steep Holm's rather arid topography, but at least can rest, and find a little food.

From late August into October, Goldcrests occur in quantity. The Goldcrest is a classic example of under-recording. The first-ever record for Steep Holm was not until 1951, but in 1975 hundreds were present in September, and their passage nowadays is certainly regular. Nationally, Goldcrest populations fluctuate considerably and in the mid-1970s their numbers were exceptionally high generally, but there is no doubt large movements occurred in the past when there was no-one there to record them. In September, 1910, for example, a considerable passage was noted at Flat Holm Lighthouse. "Large numbers" were there on 10 September. The same movement would probably have crossed Steep Holm.

Large flocks of Swallows, many House Martins and a few Sand Martins pass through in August and September. A scattering of Tree Pipits and Yellow Wagtails in the early part of the autumn is followed later by a constant stream of Meadow Pipits, sometimes several hundred per day, interspersed with Pied and Grey Wagtails. Skylarks pass through regularly in the latter half of the season but, like the pipits and wagtails, are unlikely to stay for long unless forced to by a deterioration in the weather.

With the smaller species comes a sprinkling of birds of prey. Kestrels are frequent. Sparrowhawks are less common, but probably occur annually and often several are recorded in one year. Excitement mounts when a Merlin scatters the Meadow Pipits—but could it be that they, too, are regular migrants? In half a minute a Merlin can be in from the sea, clipping the elder tops, scattering potential victims, and off out to sea again and can easily be missed altogether. Other raptors occur on occasion, ranging from the uncommon sight of a Buzzard to the rare occurrences of Hobby, Hen Harrier and Osprey. Peregrines, of course, are regular visitors in autumn and winter and one, occasionally two, may then be seen at any time.

As the autumn draws on, quiet October mornings bring vast flocks of finches— up to three thousand or more in a morning. Linnets, Goldfinches, Greenfinches, Chaffinches and a sprinkling of Redpolls, Siskins, Yellowhammers and Reed Buntings fill the air with their various calls. By midday, the island will be quiet again, with perhaps a flock of Goldfinches feeding on the thistle-heads as the only reminder of the morning's 'rush-hour'.

Waders occasionally turn up on the shore, but suitable areas for most species are rather limited and the food supply is restricted compared to the mainland shores and estuaries. Apart from the local movements of Oystercatchers, the most likely species to arrive is the Common Sandpiper, a small number occurring most years on autumn passage. Other species infrequently make short stops—half a dozen others have been recorded as doing so, including the Purple Sandpiper.

Rarities turn up on Steep Holm, as would be expected, but 'rare' is a comparative status and some of the birds which are not often recorded may be relatively common species on the mainland, such as the Tree Creeper. Some infrequent species are probably more frequent on passage than existing records would suggest, such as the Ring Ouzel and Grasshopper Warbler but others, like the Iceland Gull and the Melodious Warbler, are genuine rarities.

In winter . . . who can tell what we miss in winter? The storms of January may well bring unexpected visitors to the island, with no-one to see them. The winter regulars certainly occur on passage. Late autumn and early spring visits catch the vanguard or tail-end of the Redwing, Fieldfare and Brambling movements, but only time will tell what else flies through.

One of the more recent and most remarkable of Steep Holm bird phenomena is the scale of nightly Starling roosts and the confusion they have caused. In 1976 they caused repeated alarms that Steep Holm was on fire. At dusk thousands of Starlings converge on the east end of the island and are visible from the seafront at Weston as a dark black mass rising and swirling above the top of the island. One evening their movements appeared so constant, in the form of a column a hundred feet high and forty feet across, that even the Trust's boatmen were prepared to believe the island was burning. John Watts and Rachel Hayward, taking a late evening party of holidaymakers for a boat trip to Brean Down, watched a 'snake' of Starlings a quarter of a mile in length and ten feet wide preparing to cross to the island. One summertime count in 1976 reached 8,000 and was a conservative estimate. Numbers must often exceed ten thousand. Their main roost area is in the Sycamore wood at the north-east corner of the island, where the ground is covered with droppings sometimes more than a quarter inch in thickness, though the birds' perching preferences can change each night. There are no references to Starling

Some birds go, but others come. Rev. F.L. Blathwayt predicted in 1906 that the Firecrest would one day be caught on the island. Tony Parsons proved him right in 1975.

roosts on the island in any published bird reports.

No account of the birds would be complete without a mention of some of the observers. Reverend F. L. Blathwayt, who compiled the notes on birds for Somerset's *Victoria County History*, knew the island well in the early years of the 20th century, as did Colonel H. G. Lascelles in the years following the First World War. Blathwayt showed his appreciation of the island's importance when he wrote, in 1906, of the possibility of adding records of species such as the Firecrest and Red-breasted Flycatcher to Somerset's list by observation there. Circumstances have changed, but the Firecrest was a visitor in 1975 and 1976.

Colonel Lascelles records that he reported a Welshman to the Society for the Protection of Birds in 1921 for shooting a hen Peregrine, which was believed to be the Steep Holm breeding female. The culprit was only fined ten shillings, but fortunately the tiercel on the island found a new mate the following year. The Sleemans who were the tenants of the island, helped with occasional records of birds—including one of an eagle which flew past when Thomas was mending the Barracks roof (a frequent pastime on Steep Holm). The general consensus of opinion was that the bird was a White-tailed Eagle, a species unlikely to appear in future Steep Holm records. A male Corncrake was shot on Steep Holm on 23 April 1918. One of the islanders, Mrs Evelyn Smith, sent it to Dr J. Wiglesworth of Winscombe for his collection.

Some degree of protection for the birds occurred in the mid-twenties, when the Sleemans left the island unoccupied. After their house had been looted, the Weston magistrates promised imprisonment "without the option of a fine" to anyone caught trespassing on the island. The problem of theft and vandalism has always been a threat if the island is left unoccupied, as members of the Gull Research Station found out when the Barracks was raided in their absence.

Stanley Lewis, a frequent visitor between the wars, wrote the first comprehensive account of the birds in *British Birds* in 1936. Blathwayt, Lascelles and Lewis, together with Harry Cox and half a dozen other ornithologists supplied most of the records for the first forty years of this century. Cox, whose memorial stands on the Garden Battery, supplied many records in the years before the Second World War, while lessee of the island.

During the Second World War it is difficult to know what happened, but despite wartime killings the Steep Holm Peregrines were present in the breeding season for several years after the war, although no direct evidence of breeding was ever published. Records may have been suppressed, to lessen the risk of disturbance, as in 1954 Edmund Mason told the Society for the Promotion of Nature Reserves that the birds were nesting: "In recent years the Peregrine has returned and makes its eyrie on the steep northern cliffs in close company with a large colony of Cormorants."

In the late 1940s, boat visits started again. The Steep Holm Trust took a 21-year lease on the island and much work on the gulls and passerines, and on some other aspects of the island's biology, was done through a Gull Research Station during the next two decades. Ray Poulding, who has probably done more biological studies on the island than anyone else, wrote in September 1975 that "much of the data collected by members has unfortunately been dispersed and no central

Craggy north face of Steep Holm, the principal Cormorant cliffs of the Bristol Channel, and the place where Edmund Mason last saw a Peregrine eyrie, in 1954.

duplicate collection was made", but he hopes further papers may yet be published. His work in 1963 showed for the first time a possible method of ageing Dunnocks by their iris colour. This characteristic is now widely used by ringers. Another advance was made in Poulding's use of extruded plastics for the colour marking of gulls.

Natural history records for Steep Holm can be identified and extracted from national works such as *The Atlas of Breeding Birds in Britain and Ireland* (1976), as the island is the only land in its ten-kilometre Ordnance Survey grid-square, the unit of area on which the 'spot method' of map recording is based. Steep Holm has 26 entries in the bird atlas, compared with 39 for Lundy. The Steep Holm records are incorporated in the island's checklist, but unless they are qualified with a symbol showing confirmed breeding they can only be taken as indicating that a species was observed in the breeding season, in one or more years between 1968 and 1972. This summary of ornithological knowledge concerning Steep Holm has been compiled by the island's ringing team, with help from Peter Ferns.

Tony Parsons hangs his catch from a mist net in the twigs of an elder (left). In the other picture he is extracting a small bird from the netting. The birds are then ringed, weighed and released.

Checklist of birds recorded on Steep Holm

Key

B	breeds
E	has bred in the past
V	migrant or non-breeding visitor
U	escaped or feral birds
*	island record in The Atlas of Breeding Birds in Britain and Ireland
C	likely to be seen at the right season
O	likely to be seen at some time in most years
I	likely to be seen at some time in some years
R	unlikely to be seen under normal circumstances
?	doubtful record

Fulmar	V O	*	Whimbrel	V I	
Manx Shearwater	?E V O	offshore	Woodcock	V R	
Storm Petrel	V R	offshore	Arctic Skua	V R	offshore
Gannet	V I	offshore	Black-headed Gull	V O	
Cormorant	B C	*	Lesser Black-backed Gull	B C	*
Shag	V I		Herring Gull	B C	*
Heron	V I		Iceland Gull	V R	
Red-breasted Goose	U R		Glaucous Gull	V R	
Shelduck	B C	*	Great Black-backed Gull	B C	*
Mallard	E V I	*	Common Gull	V I	
Pochard	V R	offshore	Kittiwake	E V O	offshore
Eider	V I	offshore	Sandwich Tern	V I	offshore
Common Scoter	V O	offshore	Common/Arctic Tern	V I	offshore
Long-tailed Duck	V R	offshore	Razorbill	E V R	offshore
Osprey	V R		Guillemot	E V R	offshore
Sparrowhawk	V O		Puffin	E V R	offshore
Buzzard	V I		Woodpigeon	B C	*
White-tailed Eagle	?V R		Stock Dove	B C	*
Hen Harrier	V R		Feral Pigeon	U C	
Peregrine	E V C		Collared Dove	V I	
Hobby	V R		Turtle Dove	V I	
Merlin	V R		Cuckoo	V I	
Kestrel	E V C	*	Short-eared Owl	V R	
Water Rail	V R		Little Owl	?E V I	
Corncrake	V R		Nightjar	V R	*
Oystercatcher	E V C	*	Swift	V C	
Dotterel	V R		Alpine Swift	V R	
Golden Plover	V R		Green Woodpecker	V R	
Lapwing	V I	*	Woodlark	V R	
Turnstone	V I		Skylark	E V C	*
Purple Sandpiper	V R		Sand Martin	V C	
Dunlin	V I		Swallow	V C	
Sanderling	V R		House Martin	V C	
Redshank	V I		Tree Pipit	V O	
Common Sandpiper	V O		Meadow Pipit	E V C	*
Curlew	V I		Rock Pipit	B C	*

Yellow Wagtail	V O		Blackbird	B V C	*
Grey Wagtail	V C		Redwing	V O	
Pied Wagtail	V C		Song Thrush	B V C	*
Dipper	V R		Mistle Thrush	V O	
Wren	B C	*	Long-tailed Tit	V R	
Dunnock	B C	*	Coal Tit	V I	
Grasshopper Warbler	V O		Blue Tit	E V C	
Sedge Warbler	V O		Great Tit	V O	
Reed Warbler	V I		Tree Creeper	V R	
Melodious Warbler	V R		Yellowhammer	V I	
Garden Warbler	V O		Reed Bunting	V I	
Blackcap	V O		Chaffinch	?B V C	
Whitethroat	E V O	*	Brambling	V I	
Lesser Whitethroat	V O		Greenfinch	B V C	
Willow Warbler	V C		Siskin	V O	
Chiffchaff	V C		Goldfinch	V C	
Goldcrest	V C		Linnet	E V C	*
Firecrest	V I		Redpoll	V O	
Pied Flycatcher	V O		Bullfinch	V I	
Spotted Flycatcher	E V O		House Sparrow	V I	
Whinchat	V I		Tree Sparrow	V I	
Stonechat	V O		Starling	B V C	*
Wheatear	E V O		Magpie	E V R	
Black Redstart	V R		Jackdaw	B V C	*
Redstart	V O		Rook	V R	
Robin	B C	*	Carrion Crow	B V C	*
Fieldfare	V I		Raven	E V C	*
Ring Ouzel	V I				

Gullery social life

Colin Graham

THE SIZE of Steep Holm's gullery has made the island an ideal place for the study of these birds, and this information is helping to clarify the national picture. The Herring Gull *Larus argentatus*, is currently one of the most adaptable and therefore most successful birds in the world. From being a wary cliff bird it has adopted man as its provider of food and scavenges urban rubbish tips and port fisheries. Birds have been seen too bloated to move. Nesting on buildings, dismissed in 1944 as having happened "once on a house-roof in Devon," has become commonplace in Cardiff and many other coastal towns. The rooftop colony in Dover has 1,500 breeding pairs. It can nest beside pigeons.

The trend is international: the New England population was recorded as a maximum of 8,000 pairs in 1900 and in 1965 the figure was about 120,000. In Britain the Herring Gull numbers have doubled since the Second World War, reaching in 1970 an estimated 334,000 pairs. This figure does not include non-breeding birds. Increases in the last five years may have pushed the total number of birds to over a million, and have forced ornithologists into a control programme to protect colonies of other seabirds.

Colour-marking of the Steep Holm Herring Gulls, in operation for some years, showed the birds fly daily to rubbish tips at Barry, Cardiff, Weston-super-Mare and other points on both sides of the Bristol Channel. Offal is carried to the island in the breeding season along with the carcases of small mammals and, in particular, moles. Although moles have never been recorded alive on Steep Holm their remains are found so commonly on the paths and at nests, sometimes uneaten, that some observers have suggested the animal exists on the island after all. Against this, Tinbergen says: "Moles are almost certainly caught alive and killed by gulls."

Tinbergen, in *The Herring Gull's World*, also lists rats, young rabbits, young birds and even young cats as being taken by Dutch birds he studied. Although myxomatosis is the major cause of fluctuation in the Steep Holm rabbit population there is little doubt that the Herring Gulls are a contributory factor to the reduction. A newly-dead weasel was found on an island path in 1975.

Vegetable food taken by the Steep Holm birds includes seeds and grasses but although they are frequently seen tugging at the lower foliage of the Alexanders this is not thought to form a part of their diet. It is normally shredded and used as nest-lining material or, as with grass, is pulled as a displacement activity during the frequent threat displays that take place at territorial boundaries.

The gulls take whatever seafood they can obtain, even tugging limpets off the rocks at low tide and swallowing them whole, though the shell is later regurgitated in the pellet. To an extent though, this is limited by the lack of fish finding their way into these higher reaches of the Bristol Channel. Probably the commonest fish taken is the Sprat (*Sprattus sprattus*) which at its maximum grows no longer than about 16.5cms and is usually about 12-13cm. Food preferences change seasonally according to what is available (the sprat, for instance, swims at a depth of 10-50 metres in summer and 150 metres in winter) and the easiest check on the situation is to examine pellets cast by the gulls around nests. Pellets are regurgitated and contain the shells, seed husks, feathers, fur and bones that the bird is unable to digest.

The nearest island gulleries to Steep Holm and Flat Holm are Stert Island (ten miles south in Bridgwater Bay) which had an estimated 3,000-odd pairs in 1970, and the islands of Skokholm and Skomer off the Pembrokeshire coast about 100

A cloud of gulls and Flat Holm, seen from the northern cliffs of Steep Holm. The neighbouring island now also suffers from gulls. An immature bird, top-heavy and brown (right), will join them when it fully reaches maturity in three years time.

miles to the west. In 1970 the Skokholm breeding pairs were estimated at 1,350 and Skomer had about 2,200 pairs, the chief dietary constituent here being fish taken from the Milford Haven fish dock area ten miles away.

Despite their apparent readiness to colonise new areas, Herring Gulls are basically sedentary birds with a fairly restricted dispersal area. However, it is reasonable to suppose a certain inter-relationship exists between the western gulleries.

As far as dispersal is concerned, ringing recoveries reveal that the area concerned is seldom more than 100 miles in radius. "Operation Seafarer" which mapped and counted all British seabird colonies in 1969-70 found that gulls "breeding in Pembrokeshire move east along the south coast of Wales to the Bristol Channel and south to Devon and Cornwall, with few recoveries elsewhere."

Recoveries from gulls ringed on Steep Holm have also reflected this pattern, with about 85 per cent remaining in the Bristol Channel area. The Steep Holm Gull Research Station ringed birds throughout the 1950s and 1960s and had returns from such places as Shoreham in Sussex (125 miles), Beaminster and Bridport in Dorset (50 miles), Hayling Island in Hampshire (98 miles) and Skomer Island; the latter was unusual in that the bird concerned was ringed on Steep Holm as an adult and the movement of adult birds between colonies is rare. An exceptional record was for a Herring Gull found near Longcroft, Stirling, on 7 August, 1958, which had been ringed three years earlier. It had flown a distance of 320 miles.

The Herring Gull tends to be conservative in its choice of mate and nest-site, returning where possible with the same bird to the same place. It is not quite as simple as that, for although they are known to live for about ten years under average conditions and do not become sexually mature until they are four years old, mortality is high and a bird may have a different mate each year. As with most birds, it is the non-breeders who are pushed out and these may be the colonisers of previously uninhabited areas.

The overflow from Steep Holm, for instance, is doubtless responsible for the huge increase in the Flat Holm gull population. One-year-old birds are seldom seen on Steep Holm and presumably remain on the mainland but analysis of the ages of Herring Gulls congregating on the "clubs" (the bare patches on the island reserved for communal "activities") has shown them drifting back as they grow older, 25 per cent of them being aged between two and four years.

Immature gulls that are not part of the sedentary "loafing" flock of non-breeders, and not engaged on inter-gullery activity, appear to take a south-eastern route away from Steep Holm similar to that taken by migrating passerines. The island is not merely a useful staging post for birds crossing the Bristol Channel. In 1963 the Gull Research Station reported: "The trans-Channel route Lavernock–the Holms–Brean Down, is now recognised as an important west coast migration flight line draining Wales and in certain weather conditions the Severn Estuary coastal lines."

It seems likely both gulls and passerines follow a clearly defined route inland, as well. It would also be useful to prepare a map showing the direction taken by ringed birds. Further extensive ringing may prove Steep Holm's location is as 'strategically' as valuable as the country's most favoured observatories.

Unlike Tinbergen's sand dunes to which the Herring Gulls timidly return each spring and depart in autumn, Steep Holm is a winter roost as well as a summer nursery. Initially, the gulls nested exclusively on the island cliff-faces but the population explosion caused them to seek territories elsewhere and the central plateau was colonised. The nest is prepared (rather than built) in April and sometimes consists of no more than a scrape in the earth which is then lined with shredded grasses, Alexanders and any other plants the birds can find. The contest for space is so fierce that every open surface is taken and nests are often no more than two feet apart. This leads to highly unusual nest-locations, since the gulls build on the paths, in the ruined gun emplacements and searchlight posts, on flights of steps down the cliff-face, almost beneath the 19th century guns and even on the beach where low tides for a few days encourage them to stake out territories—only to have all swept away by the next high water.

The first eggs are laid at the end of April, usually on alternate days, until the clutch of three is complete. The colours range from olive to umber brown and are spotted and blotched with a deep blackish-brown. Occasionally the eggs are pale blue. One aspect of behaviour at this stage deserves study and that is the habit with some gulls of placing large egg-sized stones in the nest alongside the eggs. In the 1975 season about six nests were discovered that contained two eggs and one pebble. Bizarre plastic objects, particularly small children's toys, are retrieved from mainland tips and brought to the island in quantity. Many of these 'ornaments' are dropped on to the ground, but though they are not incorporated into the structure

Newly hatched Herring Gull chick still with wet feathers. One of the other eggs (top) is already pierced and the nestling will soon break through.

of the nests, sometimes one is placed next to the eggs. A nest at Split Rock in June 1977 contained two eggs, one large snail, and a decapitated doll's head. The latter was two inches high, of a human male, with a pink plastic face, prominent blue eyes and fuzzy brown hair.

Incubation, normally by both birds, lasts about 28 days. The downy chicks remain in or near the nest until they are fledged at about seven weeks of age. In that time they only leave the nest-site when danger threatens at which they scuttle in an ungainly way into the Privet, Elder, Bramble and Alexanders.

The Alexanders are currently the major control factor in the gull population, a mild winter giving the plant the opportunity to establish itself on potential nesting areas. Conversely, a hard and prolonged winter presents the Herring Gull with infinitely more space for breeding and rather than expand individual territories to absorb this extra land new birds move in and create new territories. This strong inter-relationship between plant and bird makes it impossible for one to be controlled without the other. Paradoxically, the Alexanders plant is of great importance as far as the Herring Gull is concerned later in the year for it provides essential cover for the young birds. In 1959, for example, breeding success on the plateau was not as great as in the previous year and it was reasoned that the cause lay in the early dying-off of the leaf stems of the Alexanders.

If 6,500 pairs of gulls (taking the 1976 figure) lay an average of three eggs per nest then 19,500 eggs are produced on Steep Holm each spring. These days they are seldom salty, as few gulls catch fish any longer. As Tinbergen was quick to point out they are "a perfect food" if eaten whilst fresh, being twice the size of a

A perfectly healthy gull sits on its nest. However there are occasional casualties amongst adult gulls and some that can be approached are dying of peritonitis.

hen's egg and correspondingly tastier. However, it is not a pleasure to be taken lightly, as hepatitis can be contracted. The gourmet's 'gull egg' has always been that of the Black-headed Gull.

The mortality rate from laying through hatching to fledging must be a minimum of 50 per cent of the total eggs laid or there would be a population explosion of fantastic proportions. The likelihood of high mortality increases for the nests on less suitable ground, such as among bushes, compared with the prime sites on cliffs.

Dr. J. V. Beer studied chick mortality on Steep Holm in the 1960s and discovered a number of apparent causes. He found that sudden heavy rain led to pulmonary conditions and sometimes pneumonia. A fungus *Aspergillus fumigatus* can attack the respiratory system and cause death, especially during feathering. Birds straying into foreign territories are savagely attacked and die from wounds inflicted by the adult's sharp hooked beak. And then: "As the birds grow older they may suffer from a variety of diseases, often bacterial, such as avian tuberculosis, and infections of the pericardium, the sac containing the heart. Again more die of injury."

Dr Beer also mentions the egg or yolk peritonitis that has been noticed in adult Steep Holm gulls. This condition only occurs at the beginning of the egg-laying season and is due either to the impaction of an egg in the oviduct or the rupture of a yolk-sac, the contents of which pass into the abdominal cavity causing inflammation and, finally, peritonitis.

These dead birds "can be found on their nests, sitting in a natural position, appearing to be asleep".

Dr Beer postulates that territorial fighting may be the cause of the yolk-sac rupture.

Finally, he points out, although there has been no detailed work on parasites, the research which has so far been conducted on the island's gulls, both chicks and adults, shows these are very few and relatively unimportant.

The food given to the Herring Gull chicks is always half-digested by the adult birds before it is offered. To obtain the food the chicks indulge in what must be now one of the best known aspects of animal behaviour since Pavlov's dogs—they tap the red patch on the parent's bill and this stimulus causes the adult to regurgitate. This was first noticed and recorded by the German biologist F Goethe in 1937, who presented chicks with different coloured artificial beaks. Young birds hatched in an incubator who had never seen another Herring Gull in their lives responded 181 times to a normal gull head, but only 58 times to a head with an all-yellow bill.

For many weeks the chicks are virtually indistinguishable from the chicks of their nearest relative, the Lesser Black-backed Gull (*Larus fuscus*). Dr. Jim Flegg, former director of the British Trust for Ornithology and one of the Trust's patrons, wrote in 1969: "The Lesser Black-backed Gull—sometimes called the yellow-legged herring gull—shares a circumpolar distribution, and a resulting taxonomic complexity, with the Herring Gull. From west to east, the Lesser Black-backed, the Palearctic representative of this complex, gradually approaches the plumage and leg coloration of the Herring Gull, whose stronghold is in North America, and it is in western Europe and the British Isles that the two extremes of this 'ring' meet."

Westward Television films two Lesser Black-back gull chicks at Split Rock. Chicks of the Lesser Black-back are virtually indistinguishable from those of the Herring Gull.

Perhaps the major difference between the two gulls is that one is curiously sedentary whilst the other is a summer visitor to Britain. R. K. Murton, in *Man and Birds*, wrote: "That interspecific competition between these two gulls is important during the winter is shown by the fact that the Herring Gull manages to remain a complete resident, whereas virtually all Lesser Black-backs move south to winter on the Iberian coast."

Unlike many interspecific hybrids, the young resulting from these mixed marriages are not only fertile but have been known to breed successfully with other gulls. Tinbergen explains that "this means that the mating behaviour-patterns have not yet been sufficiently differentiated" and believes that as it only occurs "when a Lesser Black-backed Gull attaches itself to a colony where there is no conspecific mate available" it is a "phenomenon typical of pioneer populations" and will decrease as Lesser Black-backed colonies grow in number. Although there appear to be no records of this occurring on Steep Holm, the ratio of one bird's population to the other on the island is such that the possibility cannot be ignored and observers would do well to make notes on any pure *fuscus* birds that are seen.

The juveniles retain their brown mottled plumage until they are three years old and it is not until then that the majority return to Steep Holm. The reason for the complete difference in plumage between the immature birds and the adults is believed to be an evolutionary throwback to the days when the juveniles fed almost exclusively on the mud-flats of the inter-tidal zone and were open to predation by skuas and the white-tailed eagle. The adults favour different feeding grounds (or used to), namely the sea itself, where white plumage against the sun makes fish-catching that much simpler. By contrast, oceanic feeders like the Kittiwake have white underparts and head from their first juvenile plumage.

Herring Gulls are intelligent. They are one of the few creatures, apart from man, who have developed the ability to use a tool in their quest for food, albeit in this case an innate one. They break the shells of cockles by dropping them from a height onto hard surfaces, though immature birds, until they have learnt this practice, have been known to spend hours dropping shells into shallow water and then taking them up again.

They indulge in "paddling" to catch earthworms, the stamping of their feet causing the earth to quiver sufficiently to bring prey to the surface. A novel variation on this was recently recorded in Britain from studying the activities of the Rook and the Carrion Crow in their feeding habits beside motorways, where the constant rumble of passing traffic has the same effect as "paddling".

An example of the Herring Gulls' capability for sudden adaptation is its perching on trees and bushes, a habit which has been forced upon it on Steep Holm by the struggle for space. The 1944 revised edition of Witherby's "Handbook" states: "Exceptionally recorded as perching in trees (not in British Isles)". And concerning the Lesser Black-back: "I am not aware of records of (it) perching in trees." Yet this is now a common sight on the island.

The intra-specific behaviour of the Herring Gull, particularly in the breeding season, is almost totally based on aggression. Irrespective of sex, one gull approaching another will be met with the threat posture, a position where the bird stretches itself up, holds its head high and makes choking movements with head and neck. If the birds are both male then this can devolve into the displacement activity of frantic grass-pulling with occasional short rushes at each other. Eventually, one bird submits and, by flattening the plumage and lowering the head, makes itself look as small as possible. The head and neck will be stretched forward horizontally and the wings are spread very slightly. 'Presenting' it is called, and male submission by the adoption of female positions is found in ape, monkey and human.

Fights frequently take place and the gulls use their wings, feet and hooked beaks to press home the attack though this is usually more a case of bluff than anything else: regular blood-letting and battles ending in death for one or both participants would obviously be harmful to the colony as a whole, though fighting gulls have been seen on Steep Holm with badly gashed heads.

If, however, the bird approaching an aggressive male is a female who does not respond to his threat posture—and release in him the further stimuli necessary for attack—he is temporarily non-plussed and the next move is hers. She stands cowed and submissive and if the male finds her sexually attractive and is unattached he approaches her. Dr. Flegg writes: "On this very flimsy platform the pair-bond begins to form, but at this early stage it is very easily disrupted unless the female maintains a submissive attitude."

Throughout the breeding season (the Herring Gull is single-brooded) a continual process of learning takes place, to the extent that, as Tinbergen discovered, the gulls not only recognise their mates but even their neighbours and frequently allow what we as human beings would describe as "personal feelings" to play a part in their everyday behaviour. Some birds are far more readily attacked than others and for

Top: The watching eye of a Steep Holm Herring Gull in flight. Despite the photograph, the underwing plumage is white.
Bottom: Proving the textbooks wrong, a Lesser Black-backed gull sits in a tree. Now a few of them go even further and nest in the branches of Steep Holm elders.

no apparent reason. Tinbergen concluded there was a personal "hatred" involved between certain individuals. One gull can recognise another.

The Herring Gull is conservative in many aspects of its behaviour and regards "outcasts" with a fear manifested in aggression. Man's inhumanity to minority groups is a comparable example. There is a report from Steep Holm of the capture of an adult Lesser Black-backed Gull whose flight was weak, whose plumage was dirty and who appeared not merely to be sick but probably close to death. When the bird was released it flew off down the cliff and over the sea, and immediately, two or three Herring Gulls rose and chased after it. The bird was persistently followed and attacked by two of the gulls long after it had cleared the nesting sites and general congregating areas and finally vanished out to sea, still trying to avoid the attacks of a pursuing gull.

It had not apparently transgressed any gull law, though there are similar instances of such behaviour recorded by Tinbergen, where Herring Gulls proved hostile towards one of their number which had been captured for ringing and just released. Tinbergen concluded that study of this phenomenon "would be very worth while, because (it) has interesting sociological aspects".

Information here presented on gull behaviour comes primarily from studies made before about 1950, the period when the Herring Gull had only just begun to expand its range and was learning to adapt to new and widely differing conditions. Much of the work on Steep Holm has been concerned, not unnaturally, with population dynamics to the apparent exclusion of the "new" science of ethology. Sufficient evidence has already been presented to demonstrate that the Herring Gull has undergone behaviour changes in the last 30 years.

Like leisured elderly gentlemen, the Herring Gulls have their "clubs", a term coined by Tinbergen to describe those areas within the gullery that are free of nests (or should be) and which also lack most of the territorial restrictions that are imposed on every other square inch of the colony. There are at least half-a-dozen of these on Steep Holm but the inaccessibility of some and the inconsistency of size of others makes it difficult to provide a concise figure. Two of these "clubs" are situated on the central plateau immediately north of the Barracks. The entire plateau is essentially the domain of the Alexanders, which here grow to shoulder-height, thanks to the guanoed soil with its rich nitrates and phosphates.

Despite this the gulls have managed to keep these two areas completely clear of every shred of vegetation and it is here that the non-breeders may be found, posturing frantically in their search for a mate. However, demand for space became so great on the island that in 1976 nests were scattered arbitrarily throughout these two particular "club" areas and it will be interesting to see which aspect of gull life, breeding or "clubbing", wins through.

Two other Steep Holm "clubs" are worth mentioning: one because it lies astride a main path and cannot be missed and the other because its inaccessible position on the cliff-face means it will be totally overlooked. The first is about 200 yards west of the Barracks building on the short-turfed hummock facing seaward at Split Rock battery. The second is almost immediately below the Barracks, though again slightly to the west, and lies on a less steep gradient of the cliff-face not far above high-water mark. This can really only be seen from the sea.

To the untrained ear the call-notes of the Herring Gull seem to be no more than a succession of loud harsh cries, uttered constantly and for no apparent reason whatsoever. This is particularly true of Steep Holm where the exceedingly high numbers inevitably mean there is continuous calling. So much hectic activity takes place at the height of the breeding season, for instance, that even the approach of nightfall does nothing to silence the clamour. It is strangely uncanny to see thousands of ghostly Herring Gulls at two o'clock in the morning, flying by the light of the moon and calling as loudly as ever. At this time of year the colony is active 24 hours a day.

Tinbergen, who describes the Herring Gull's voice as "melodious", isolated eight different calls and attempted to define the meaning and purpose of each. There is the general call-note, a monosyllabic *keew* or *kleew* and there is the charge call when a bird is about to attack. It is a modification of the *keew* call "distinguishable by its loudness and staccato character". There is the multisyllabic trumpeting call, again based on *keew*, which begins moderately then rises to a pitch of loud resounding screams. This is characteristic of "clubbing".

Then there is the call that deceives many visitors to Steep Holm who, hearing voices in the distance, expect to come across a group of people round the next bend in the path and then wonder where they hid themselves so quickly. This strange sound, something like a rhythmical *huch-huch-huch-huch*, has come to be known as "choking" and is made primarily when a pair make a nest-scrape together. It is also used in aggressive situations and it is a hybrid of this call and the next that many of

'Club' area for Herring Gulls above the southern shore, between the clifftop and the belt of elder scrub. This patch of ground is largely free from territorial tensions and the birds are allowed a form of free association.

the Steep Holm birds use when they are preparing to attack man. At the height of the breeding season this is the call that all visitors to the island learn faster than any other and he who is slow in taking instant evasive action is likely to receive a smart clip across the head from a well-muscled wing for his carelessness. In human terms it is something like a sardonic laugh.

The alarm call is a hoarse rhythmic *hahaha!—hahahaha!* and although it is a reaction to potential danger the emphasis is laid on flight, not attack.

Then there is the "mew" call, a plaintive long-drawn note that "indicates breeding activity with the emphasis on the friendly attitude toward mate, territory, nest and young".

The begging call, made by the female at the start of the breeding season is a courtship device to encourage feeding by the male and is a soft *klee-ew*. Finally, there is the male's copulation note, another rhythmic and sometimes prolonged call that lies somewhere between the choking and alarm calls.

Tinbergen devotes a brief chapter in *The Herring Gull's World* to the sensory capacities of the bird. Can they see what we see and how good is their hearing? As far as sight is concerned it appears that their limitations regarding the colour spectrum are the same as ours. They have no more ability to see infra-red or ultra-violet than human beings and their powers of colour discrimination are probably not as advanced as ours. We know they appear to see red as a distinct colour but most workers in the field of black-and-white photography can demonstrate the simplicity of identifying primary colours in a monochrome print from the intensity of the shades of grey. Their eyesight is probably better than ours with "an amazing capacity of distinguishing between forms".

Although even less work has been performed on the Herring Gull's hearing ability than on its sight Tinbergen concluded that it was no better than our own. As far as their other senses are concerned we know they can taste the food they eat. They dislike highly salted fish, but hardly surprisingly, seem to have no sense of smell.

Finally, we come to what is probably the most important aspect of the Herring Gull and Steep Holm—its future. Hard-line ecologists believe the bird should suffer as little human interference as possible and there is no doubt that the island provides excellent opportunities for studying its life and behaviour, particularly in the light of adaptations the Herring Gull may have made in the last 25 years.

The gulls physically attack both the flora and fauna to the extent that certain plants have been totally eradicated and more will follow. They are also a threat to the island's slow-worm, which suffers considerable predation by the birds. Left to itself Steep Holm could eventually become a rocky desert with nothing other than Alexanders and Herring Gulls. A certain measure of control is essential if the island's potential is to be exploited.

R. K. Murton, in *Man and Birds*, reports on the wide variety of control methods from shooting to providing poisoned food, and by spraying the fertile eggs with a mixture of high grade oil and formaldehyde. Strychnine nitrate in Holland accounted for about 10,000 adults annually, though the programme was frequently interrupted and the populations had time to recover. It is a fact of animal life that colonies, be they bird or mammal, become self-regulating and subsequently stabilise when

A Herring Gull 'trumpets' its sardonic laugh, echoed by a neighbouring bird as a protest against human intrusion. The call begins with the head right down and ends with the beak pointing skywards.

their numbers have reached a peak.

Egg-spraying was conducted in the United States. There was a reduction in the breeding population after four years, when the immature birds should have been nesting for the first time. However, in ten years the decline ceased and it appears that the disturbance associated with the spraying caused many gulls to move elsewhere. Tinbergen also mentions various methods that were tried in an attempt to control gull numbers. Taking the eggs has no effect for the birds merely scatter and lay again further afield.

Even if sufficient nests on Steep Holm were accessible egg-pricking would be not only time-consuming but potentially ineffective, for unless done carefully, the wound in the shell heals over and the chick hatches normally. Tinbergen found that a better method was to shake the eggs some days after the onset of incubation. This killed the germ inside and the gulls continued to incubate one or two weeks in excess of the normal four-week period. After this, no second brood was attempted.

Lack of natural predators has led to the need for man to interfere. Gulls have few enemies, basically birds of prey—here mainly the Peregrine *Falco peregrinus*— the fox, and man. The fox is absent from Steep Holm and visiting Peregrines come mainly in autumn and winter. Hedgehog predation has been mentioned in the mammal chapter, but can hardly amount to more than a minor nuisance. Yet the gull population has stabilised, and may be falling, for the first time in Steep Holm's history, and it would seem man is solely responsible. Regular visiting brings disturbance, in some parts of the island reaching devastating proportions, and lowering the success rate of all birds on level ground, but generally doing nothing to harm those on the scree slopes and cliffs.

The new element of well-intentioned human predation, through the upheaval it causes, may be solving the problem for Steep Holm. Gull numbers in 1975, 1976 and 1977 decreased and as the rapid increase in breeding pairs on Flat Holm cannot be wholly attributed to a natural Steep Holm overspill it seems likely that human interference is responsible. Overall, the Steep Holm population has slumped from a record 8,500 pairs in 1975; to 6,500 pairs in 1976; and then to 4,000 pairs in 1977. The state of health of the remaining birds is greatly improved, and the island is no longer littered with corpses as it was in past years. Such overcrowding has also been followed by population crashes on the New England seaboard in America. The dramatic halving of the Steep Holm population coincided with the publication in 1977 of a Malthus-like projection by Dr. Peter Ferns and Greg Mudge suggesting that the island gull numbers could reach an ultimate total of 50,000 pairs. The science of bird study has not yet caught up with the realities.

Herring Gulls are not a new breed of super-bird, though frequent contact with them on an island such as Steep Holm makes objective appraisal difficult. Though as man-dependent as any bird they are less happy when coexistence takes place on level terms in the breeding season. Perhaps some retreat from disturbance and fly elsewhere, and although it is defeatist to solve the problem by despatching them all

Opposite: Immature Herring Gull, one of several thousand that die on the island each year. This nestling was born at South Landing in 1976 and died when its parents neglected it during that summer's fierce drought.

to Flat Holm, it is a short-term answer that will give the Trust a breathing-space and the opportunity to make plans for the future of Steep Holm. Events may in any case be overtaken by the formation of a national policy.

Below: Low-flying adult Herring Gull, coming in to 'buzz' a visitor. Sometimes the super-birds misjudge their angle of attack and collide with the tops of human heads.

An insect island

Tony Parsons

GRADUALLY, BIOLOGICAL studies on Steep Holm have expanded from the large and conspicuous birds and flowers into the world of smaller creatures. A remarkable scientific discovery was made on Steep Holm in 1972 by Dr. C. R. Bantock, a population geneticist, who spent a week studying the banded landsnails (*Cepaea nemoralis*). His principal conclusions were that the exceptional southern-oceanic climate of the island, giving rise to the unusual flora, was in turn "reflected in unusual genetic properties of the snails living in the vegetation". There is a significant geographical distribution of colour and banding on Steep Holm, apparently related to the local climate in varying parts of the island. The Steep Holm snails were "chromosomally different" from those on the mainland. Dr. Bantock, who works at the North London Polytechnic, is continuing his study and the results so far have revealed a unique situation: "This is the first time that variation of this kind has been found in this species and it is of great interest to the theory of population evolution and species formation.

"I find myself more and more intrigued by this island," Cuillin Bantock says. "So much of the fauna seems to fit in with Darwin's observations on island fauna on his voyage—large size being common where predation is low." John Fowles, a spider enthusiast, invariably disappears shortly after arriving on the island, usually down an inaccessible scree slope, where he searches under every rock. His experience is that the Steep Holm spiders are often larger than would be expected. Dr. Bantock provides another example: "I noticed that the woodlice are much bigger than on the mainland. I collected a few in 1972 and measured them. They were several millimetres bigger than the upper figure for maximum length given in the published keys."

Apart from the climatic factor, another likely reason for the development of a larger adult shell size ("greater than on both Flat Holm and the nearest point on the mainland") is the absence of significant predation. Here, however, the previous balance in favour of the snail may have been reversed. There is evidence that their competition from vertebrates has increased since Dr. Bantock's visit. The song

177

thrush population has become more noticeable as a result of the Trust's provision of standing water, and it is commonplace to find snail shells eaten out from the rear in typical hedgehog fashion, though the animals, like the island's occasional visiting Frenchmen, do seem to have a distinct preference for the garden rather than the banded species. Some gulls, too, peck through a considerable number of snails, and quantities of shells are sometimes found around nests.

Insect lists for the island are not yet exhaustive but commoner species are now reasonably well documented. Expert surveys include Hugh Boyd's work on the island's woodlice in 1949 and B. J. Chase's spider discoveries at the beginning of the 1970s. But most of our knowledge comes from random notes.

Steep Holm is an insect island. Most insects thrive in warmth and sunshine. South-slanting coasts have on average five hours of bright sunshine a day, whereas other parts of this country have less than four hours. A mild island like Steep Holm, with its principal slopes facing due south, offers optimum conditions for insects. The position is additionally interesting because of the unusual plant communities, and the introduction of parasites carried by the vast seabird population and influx of migrant birds.

Insects also migrate. Some, such as dragonflies, are easy to spot as they cross Steep Holm, and at least three species have been seen. Large movements of hover-flies, butterflies and moths are noticeable. Others are less easy to distinguish from the indigenous insect populations. The large land masses either side of the Bristol Channel have a great influence on the island's species list, as do the bird populations themselves.

Whatever fleas and lice the gulls carry, their real contribution to the insect fauna comes with their death. The summertime multitude of carcases attracts and supports vast quantities of insects. On hot days, every few feet, clouds of flies buzz around carrion. A number of true flies are closely associated with bird mortalities.

The two most abundant are probably the least popular with the public at large — a green-bottle and a blue-bottle. The green-bottle, *Lucilia sericata*, is by far the commonest fly on Steep Holm. It can be a nuisance in the Barracks at times, but on the mainland it is a serious pest economically. It is often the main cause of 'sheep-strike' where soiled sheep become infested with its maggots. By far the commonest island blue-bottle is *Calliphora vicina*; the fly the housewife angrily slaps at as it buzzes heavily around the kitchen in summer looking for uncovered delicacies on which to lay its eggs. Its old name of *C. erythrocephala* (the 'red-headed blue-bottle') is very descriptive, since the sides of the face are conspicuously red.

G. W. Parnell, on a visit in 1938, noted how the carnivorous and carrion-feeding species were increasing and the herbivorous species decreasing. Although this is probably an over-simplification, it gives a good impression of the situation as it struck a visitor. Both Parnell in 1938, and Griffiths and Bartlett in 1914, commented on the scarcity of flies. The 1914 visit was made in May, and in a period when the present huge gullery was still in its infancy, but one would have expected more flies to have been present at the July visit of 1938.

Turning over rotting carcases may not be most people's idea of an interesting hobby but to the entomologist on Steep Holm it is a sure way of finding burying beetles and other species that live in carrion. One beetle that is easily found on the ground is the Devil's Coach Horse, *Ocypus olens*. This large, black beetle has very short wing cases, and the segmented body is exposed. When disturbed, it has a habit of turning up its abdomen in a threatening gesture designed to frighten the intruder. It usually succeeds, although it is completely harmless.

Another beetle is the Seven-spot Ladybird, *Coccinella septempunctata*. In drought years, like 1975 and 1976, numbers of these can be phenomenally high, many of them being immigrants. At times the air can be thick with them and they can then be found in every part of the island, including the beach, and even floating in rafts on the sea, like lemmings bent on suicide.

As well as small numbers of the Common Field Grasshopper (*Chorthippus brunneus*) on Steep Holm, there are two species of cricket. One of these will become familiar to anyone staying overnight in autumn. The brown Dark Bush-cricket, *Pholidoptera griseoaptera*, is southern Britain's commonest bush-cricket and is very common around, and often in, the Barracks. Lying in bed with shrill chirrups coming from a few feet away is a not uncommon occurrence. The females of this and the green Speckled Bush-cricket, *Leptophyes punctatissima*, have long, curved ovipositors, and this added to their deliberate slow movements and long legs can make them appear rather menacing, but they are totally harmless. The Speckled Bush-cricket, easily distinguished on colour, has an almost inaudible song of a repetition of short chirps, and is found throughout the island's scrub but mainly in the eastern half.

Bernard Pickard, an authority on crickets, suggests that Steep Holm might be one site where a reservoir population of the Field Cricket, *Gryllus campestris*, could be established. This is rapidly becoming one of Britain's rarest crickets, and initial examination of the situation on Steep Holm indicates that the island could well be suitable. Deliberate introductions of this type must be carefully assessed, in particular to avoid disturbing the ecological balance. This balance itself is never stable, but is in constant flux. Such introductions must also be carefully documented, for the benefit of future studies.

A relative of the crickets, the Lesser Cockroach, *Ectobius panzeri*, was recorded in 1938. Before visitors recoil in horror, it must be emphasised that this is not the household pest variety. It lives in a wide variety of habitats, preferring coastal situations. If it still occurs on Steep Holm, this would be its northernmost stronghold in the Bristol Channel, its nearest known habitats being North Devon and Carmarthen. Although the males can fly, the females are flightless.

The flightless insects and many of the other small creatures such as the woodlice, centipedes and land snails are of particular interest since they should in theory have been present on the island since its separation from the mainland. There is, unfortunately, one factor on Steep Holm which makes any such assumption very hypothetical. The gulls constantly bring material from the mainland, particularly carcases. Their favourites are moles and poultry remains and it is possible invertebrates or their eggs could be transported to the island in this way. It seems certain that myxomatosis was introduced in this fashion. The virus is carried by the rabbit flea, *Spilopsyllus cuniculi*, which can be found in large numbers on freshly dead rabbits on the island. Infective fleas were probably introduced on rabbit remains brought from the mainland.

The butterflies and larger moths, in human terms, are the most popular of insects, and can occur in very large numbers at times. Numbers fluctuate markedly since the majority are migrants. Small numbers of larvae and pupae of a few species can be found, but the swarms of Large and Small White Butterflies and Silver Y-Moths which occur at times are composed largely of immigrants. In fine weather in autumn, many hundreds of butterflies may occur at one time, of several species, although the really abundant species are the two 'whites', the Red Admiral and the Small Tortoiseshell.

Investigation of the underground magazines of the gun batteries can be fruitful. Numbers of butterflies and moths, in particular Red Admirals, Small Tortoiseshells, Peacocks and Herald Moths can be found here in hibernation, apparently undeterred by numerous Culvert Spiders, *Meta menardi*, whose large white egg-cocoons festoon the magazines. This species, a relative of the orb-web spinners common to every garden is strongly photophobic, or light-shunning. One also encounters small numbers of mosquitoes here, and at times also around the Barracks. The common *Culex pipiens* and *Culiseta annulata* both occur, the latter having white rings around its legs. It is appreciated that the victim of either of these species will probably not worry too much about the colour of the legs, but neither species is generally numerous, though they were locally present in quantity in the underground magazine chambers in December 1976. Their origin remains a mystery at present, there being no obvious breeding situation on the island. Examination of the underground water tank has so far produced no evidence of breeding, and there is no open water on the island other than occasional brackish spray pools on the cliffs. Perhaps they, too, are immigrants.

As well as the Culvert Spider, there are several other unusual species on the island. The Purse-web Spider, *Atypus affinis*, lives in a sealed, silken tube from six inches to approaching two feet in length, the majority of which is buried. The spider captures its prey by striking through the wall of the tube with its specially adapted fangs, then drawing the captive through the tube. The damage is then repaired as soon as the prey has been taken to the bottom of the tube. Sample digging in 1969 provided an estimate of 5,000 Purse-web Spiders in the scree slopes above Calf Rock.

Two other spiders of the many recorded are rather rare nationally. The six-eyed *Segestria bavarica* has specialised requirements of habitat, with a preference for rocks and cliff crevices above the splash zone, and on Steep Holm is common on the southern cliffs. The squat *Oxyptila blackwalli*, only found in coastal areas of the southern counties, has been likened to a tiny toad. Its discovery on Steep Holm in 1969 was the first time it had been found in Somerset.

In summer and autumn an itch on the legs indicates an encounter with the abundant Harvest Mite, *Trombicula autumnalis*. It is the tiny orange-red larva which penetrates the top layers of the skin and produces an intense irritation. The best antidote is to swab the affected areas with methylated spirit, and the only consolation is that most of the irritation will have subsided in twenty-four hours. Amazingly, affected birds on Steep Holm, which include virtually all the Dunnocks and Blackbirds, seem to be remarkably little troubled by their multitude of pas-

Sealed silken tube (left), found under a rock, was home for a Purse-web Spider. The extracted occupant (right) is a female, and she uses her fangs to strike through the tube and immobilise prey.

sengers. One Dunnock trapped in August 1976 carried about 500 mite larvae, but seemed perfectly healthy. When retrapped in October, it only had about a dozen mites and the feathers had grown over the originally bare, mite-infested areas. Even the island's rabbits and hedgehogs carry a moderate quota of the mites.

Some of the birds, particularly the Blackbirds, also carry ticks. These are of a species known as *Ixodes frontalis*, related to the common sheep-tick, and they seem to be relatively common on the island.

There are many more insects yet to be found on Steep Holm—for example only one species of book-louse has so far been identified. Yet these insects are abundant in many parts of the island (most species having no connection whatsoever with books). Small species of sawfly and ichneumon are common, but can be extremely difficult to determine. For the amateur entomologist or the experienced specialist, Steep Holm has much to offer. On a small island, collecting for its own sake could soon threaten the very existence of some species, and it is to be hoped that any biologist working on Steep Holm will always be conscious of this.

Turning to the molluscs, we find that slugs are not particularly common on the island, although two of the gardener's worst enemies, *Arion hortensis* and *Agriolimax reticulatus*, both occur. Of the land snails, the large Garden Snail, *Helix aspersa*, is common, and numerous smaller species also occur, particularly those associated with a fairly dry, limestone habitat.

We are very fortunate with Steep Holm's shore fauna. The renowned specialist Dr. C. M. Yonge spent some time at Bristol, and visited the island with the survey team in 1938. His paper, written in conjunction with colleague A. J. Lloyd, formed the third paper in a series entitled *Studies on the Biology of the Bristol Channel.* In describing the situation in the Bristol Channel, one can do no better than repeat part of Maurice Yonge's introduction to the series. "There is no region around the shores of Great Britain of greater intrinsic interest than the Bristol Channel and the estuary of the River Severn. The exceptional range of the tides and the long distances over which estuarine conditions prevail, both the result of the gradual narrowing of the Channel and estuary, combine to produce unusual hydrographic conditions which have a profound effect on the animal life. Animals living in the upper regions of the Channel and the lower region of the estuary (taking the mouth of the River Avon as the boundary between these) suffer daily the effects of wide ranges in salinity, of the backward and forward movements of the greatest tides found in Europe, and of the exposure to the abnormally heavy concentrations of silt brought down by the rivers and kept long in suspension by the violent water movements caused by the tides."

The shore fauna of the island is remarkably poor in actual number of species in comparison with other sites on adjacent coasts. There are two main factors responsible. One is the salinity of the water, which is relatively low. The other is the high turbidity of the water. Animals such as sea-urchins are unable to survive in the brackish, estuarine conditions, and most small creatures which sift food from the water with tiny waving arms (cilia) cannot function where the particles of mud are so thickly distributed.

The dominant group of animals on Steep Holm's shores is the Mollusca— the sea-shells. Although the list of one mail-shell, one whelk, two limpets and three periwinkles is a short one, four of the species are quite common and the Common Limpet is abundant.

One species of sea-anemone, the Beadlet Anemone, is relatively common, particularly high up in gulleys and cracks in the cliffs where the constant movement of the water prevents them being choked in mud. Most specimens are of the common maroon or brownish-red colour, but a few dark green ones may be found. Two other species have also been recorded. The Dahlia Anemone seems to stand up better to the mud, and may be found near the lowest tide lines. The other, scarcer, species is known by its Latin name of *Sagartia troglodytes*—literally, the cave-dweller. Yonge only found it high up in clean, clear spray-pools.

Barnacles occur in moderate numbers on some parts of the shore, and turning over stones on the less rocky parts of the beach may reveal sandhoppers of a species that prefers the brackish water conditions. Two of Steep Holm's short list of sea-weeds, the Saw Wrack and the Bladder Wrack, are abundant. The others are less frequent. A list of the seaweeds will be found in their rightful place at the end of the chapter on plants.

The island's small-fauna list compiled in 1977, gives the year when the record of each species was first published. Those shown with an asterisk are extremely doubtful, and very likely incorrect, and cannot be taken as authentic without further confirmation.

Wrack-beds and rock pools along the eastern shore. Only in this upper zone is there sufficient light for a reasonable marine fauna as well.

Checklist of the island's smaller fauna

Coelenterata
Actinia equina Linn. 1939
Tealia felina (Linn.) 1939
Sagartia troglodytes (Price) 1939

Oligochaeta
Allobophora longa Ude 1939
A. chlorotica (Savigny) 1978

Cirripedia
Balanus balanoides (Linn.) 1939

Isopoda
Ligia oceanica (Linn.) 1915
Platyarthrus hoffmannseggi Brandt 1939
Philoscia muscorum (Scopoli) 1939
Oniscus asellus Linn. 1915
*Trachelipus (?) ratzeburgi (Brandt) 1949
Metoponorthus pruinosus (Brandt) 1949
Porcellio scaber Latreille 1915
Armadillidium vulgare (Latreille) 1915
*A. pictum Brandt 1949
*A. pulchellum (Zencker) 1949
Androniscus dentiger Verhoeff 1978
Trichoniscus pusillus (Brandt) 1939
Idotea chelipes (Pallas) 1939

Amphipoda
Gammarus (? *zaddachi* Sexton) 1939

Decapoda
Carcinus maenas (Linn.) 1939

Chilopoda
Haplophilus subterraneus (Shaw) 1978
Necrophloeophagus longicornis (Leach) 1978
Cryptops hortensis Leach 1978
Lithobius variegatus Leach 1978
L. forficatus (Linn.) 1915

Diplopoda
Polydesmus angustus Latzel 1915
Blaniulus guttulatus (Bosc) 1978
Tachypodoiulus niger (Leach) 1915

INSECTA

Thysanura
Machilus maritimus (Leach) 1915
Thermobia domestica (Packard) 1978

Collembola
Anurida maritima (Guerin) 1939

Odonata
Aeshna juncea (Linn.) 1978

Libellula quadrimaculata Linn. 1978
Sympetrum striolatum (Charpentier) 1978

Plecoptera
Perla bipunctata Pictet 1978

Orthoptera
Pholidoptera griseoaptera (DeGeer) 1978
Leptophyes punctatissima (Bosc) 1978
Chorthippus brunneus (Thunberg) 1978

Dermaptera
Forficula auricularia Linn. 1915
F. lesnei Finot 1939

Dictyoptera
*Ectobius panzeri Stephens 1939

Psocoptera
Graphopsocus cruciatus (Linn.) 1978

Hemiptera : Heteroptera
Acanthosoma haemorrhoidale (Linn.) 1978
Troilus luridus (Fabricius) 1978
Heterogaster urticae (Fabricius) 1978
Anthocoris confusus Reuter 1978
A. nemorum (Linn.) 1978
Orius laevigatus (Fieber) 1978
Orius niger (Wolff) 1978
Liocoris tripustulatus (Fabricius) 1978
Lygocoris pabulinus (Linn.) 1978
Nysius thymi (Wolff) 1978

Hemiptera : Homoptera
Philaenus spumarius (Linn.) 1978
Drepanosiphum platanoides (Schrank) 1978
Aphis sambuci Linn. 1939
Brachycaudus cardui (Linn.) 1978
Hyperomyzus lactucae (Linn.) 1978
Microlophium carnosum (Buckton) 1978

Neuroptera
Hemerobius humulinus (Linn.) 1978
Kimminsia subnebulosa (Stephens) 1978
Chrysopa albolineata Killington 1978
C. carnea (Stephens) 1978
C. flavifrons (Braur) 1978
C. septempunctata Wesmael 1978

Trichoptera
Stenophylax permistus McLachlan 1978

Lepidoptera
Zygaena filipendulae (Linn.) 1915
Yponomeuta padella (Linn.) 1978
Agonopterix alstroemeriana (Clerck) 1978

Dichrorampha plumbana (Scopoli)	1915	Diptera	
Aethes francillana (Fabricius)	1957	*Tipula oleracea* Linn.	1978
Crambus pratella (Linn.)	1915	*Culiseta annulata* (Schrank)	1978
Scoparia arundinata (Thunberg)	1915	*Culex pipiens* Linn.	1978
Nomophila noctuella (Den. & Sch.)	1956	*Dilophus febrilis* (Linn.)	1915
Metriostola betulae (Goeze)	1958	*Scatopse notata* (Linn.)	1978
Colias croceus (Geof. in Four.)	1956	*Dasineura urticae* (Perris)	1978
Pieris brassicae (Linn.)	1902	*Chloromyia formosa* (Scopoli)	1978
P. rapae (Linn.)	1902	*Thereva nobilitata* (Fabricius)	1972
P. napi (Linn.)	1956	*Empis tessellata* Fabricius	1972
Lycaena phlaeas (Linn.)	1955	*Poecilobothrus nobilitatus* (Linn.)	1978
Polyommatus icarus (Rottem.)	1902	*Medetera truncorum* Meigen	1972
Celastrina argiolus (Linn.)	1955	*Lonchoptera sp.* (Unidentified)	1939
Vanessa atalanta (Linn.)	1939	*Syrphus ribesii* (Linn.)	1972
Cynthia cardui (Linn.)	1902	*S. vitripennis* Meigen	1978
Aglais urticae (Linn.)	1956	*Metasyrphus corollae* (Fabricius)	1978
Inachis io (Linn.)	1957	*M. luniger* (Meigen)	1978
Argynnis aglaja (Linn.)	1902	*Epistrophe eligans* (Harris)	1978
Pararge aegeria (Linn.)	1978	*Scaeva pyrastri* (Linn.)	1978
Lasiommata megera (Linn.)	1978	*Dasysyrphus albostriatus* (Fallen)	1978
Maniola jurtina (Linn.)	1939	*Episyrphus balteatus* (DeGeer)	1978
Coenonympha pamphilus (Linn.)	1902	*Sphaerophoria scripta* (Linn.)	1978
Malacosoma neustria (Linn.)	1902	*Platycheirus albimanus* (Fabricius)	1972
Xanthorhoe designata (Hufnagel)	1978	*P. clypeatus* (Meigen)	1978
Xanthorhoe spadicearia (Den. & Sch.)	1939	*P. scutatus* (Meigen)	1978
Epirrhoe galiata (Den. & Sch.)	1915	*Eumerus strigatus* (Fallen)	1972
Camptogramma bilineata (Linn.)	1902	*Syritta pipiens* (Linn.)	1978
Triphosa dubitata (Linn.)	1978	*Eristalis tenax* (Linn.)	1978
Philereme transversata (Hufnagel)	1978	*Eristalinus aenus* (Scopoli)	1978
Eupithecia vulgata (Haworth)	1956	*Euleia heraclei* (Linn.)	1972
E. tripunctaria (Haworth)	1957	*Chyliza extenuatum* (Rossi)	1972
Aplocera plagiata (Linn.)	1978	*Coelopa frigida* (Fabricius)	1978
Abraxas grossulariata (Linn.)	1978	*Suillia variegata* (Loew)	1972
Menophra abruptaria (Thunberg)	1955	*Palloptera umbellatarum* (Fabric.)	1972
Arctia caja (Linn.)	1954	*Lonchaea chorea* (Fabricius)	1915
Tyria jacobaeae (Linn.)	1902	*L. flavidipennis* Zetterstedt	1972
Euxoa nigricans (Linn.)	1978	*Athrycia trepida* (Meigen)	1972
Standfussiana lucernea (Linn.)	1957	*Phyto melanocephala* (Meigen)	1972
Noctua pronuba (Linn.)	1939	*Sarcophaga dissimilis* Meigen	1972
Spaelotis ravida (Den. & Sch.)	1939	*S. nigriventris* Meigen	1972
Diarsia mendica (Fabricius)	1978	*S. subvicina* Rohdendorf	1972
Eurois occulta (Linn.)	1939	*S. teretirostris* Pandelle	1972
Orthosia gothica (Linn.)	1955	*Calliphora vicina* Robineau-Desv.	1978
Mythimna pallens (Linn.)	1978	*C. vomitoria* (Linn.)	1939
Cucullia verbasci (Linn.)	1957	*Lucilia caesar* (Linn.)	1939
Amphipyra pyramidea (Linn.)	1978	*L. sericata* (Meigen)	1972
A. tragopoginis (Clerck)	1978	*Scatophaga stercoraria* (Linn.)	1978
Phlogophora meticulosa (Linn.)	1978	*Anthomyia pluvialis* (Linn.)	1978
Apamea oblonga (Haworth)	1939	*Fannia canicularis* (Linn.)	1978
Mesapamea secalis (Linn.)	1978	*Orthellia viridis* (Wiedemann)	1978
Archanara geminipuncta (Haworth)	1939	*Musca domestica* Linn.	1939
Plusia gamma (Linn.)	1915	*Hydrotaea irritans* (Fallen)	1978
Callistege mi (Clerck)	1915	*Hebecnema umbratica* (Meigen)	1978
Scoliopteryx libatrix (Linn.)	1902	*Haematobia irritans* (Linn.)	1978
Rivula sericealis (Scopoli)	1956	*Ornithomyia avicularia* (Linn.)	1978

O. fringillina Curtis	1978
*Nemopoda nitidula (Fallen)	1915

Hymenoptera

Cladius pectinicornis (Linn.)	1939
Pimpla rufata	1939
Apanteles glomeratus (Linn.)	1978
Myrmica scabrinodis Nylander	1915
Formica fusca Linn.	1915
F. lemani Bondroit	1978
*F. sanguinea Latreille	1939
Lasius alienus (Foerster)	1915
*L. brunneus (Latreille)	1939
L. flavus (Fabricius)	1915
L. niger (Linn.)	1915
Vespula sylvestris (Scopoli)	1978
Cemonus lethifer Shuck	1915
Clytochrysus cavifrons (Thoms.)	1978
Andrena haemorrhoa (Fabricius)	1956
A. nigraenea (Kirby)	1956
A. jacobi Perkins	1956
A. minutula (Kirby)	1956
Bombus lapidarius (Linn.)	1915
B. terrestris (Linn.)	1978
B. lucorum (Linn.)	1978
B. pratorum (Linn.)	1978
Nomada flava Panzer	1956

Coleoptera

Carabus violaceus Linn.	1939
Nebria brevicollis (Fabricius)	1939
N. gyllenhali (Schoenherr)	1939
Pterostichus cupreus (Linn.)	1958a
Abax parallelepipedus (Piller & Mit.)	1958a
Calathus fuscipes (Goeze)	1958a
C. melanocephalus (Linn.)	1958a
Amara communis (Panzer)	1915
Harpalus affinis (Schrank)	1915
H. rufibarbis (Fabricius)	1915
H. seladon (Schauffer)	1958a
Badister bipustulatus (Fabricius)	1958a
Brachinus crepitans (Linn.)	1915
Hister ?bissexstriatus Fabricius	1939
H. unicolor Linn.	1939
Nicrophorus humator (Gleditsch)	1939
N. vestigator Herschel	1939
Proteinus ovalis Stephens	1958a
Medon brunneus (Erichson)	1958a
Xantholinus linearis (Olivier)	1958a
Staphylinus globulifer (Geoff. in Fourc.)	1915
S. olens Muller	1915
Tachyporus nitidulus (Fabricius)	1958a
Dinaraea angustula (Gyllenhal)	1958a
Atheta fungi (Gravenhorst)	1958a
Drusilla canaliculata (Fabricius)	1958a
Aleochara curtula (Goeze)	1915

Melolontha melolontha (Linn.)	1939
Phyllopertha horticola (Linn.)	1957
Syncalypta striatopunctata Steff.	1915
Agrypnus murinus (Linn.)	1915
Melanotus erythropus (Gmel. in Linn.)	1915
Athous haemorrhoidalis (Fabricius)	1978
Meligethes obscurus Erichson	1915
Omosita colon (Linn.)	1958
Rhyzobius litura (Fabricius)	1958a
Adonia variegata (Goeze)	1939
Adalia decempunctata (Linn.)	1978
Coccinella septempunctata Linn.	1958
Lagria hirta (Linn.)	1978
Oedemera nobilis (Scopoli)	1957
Longitarsus jacobaeae (Waterhouse)	1978
Sphaeroderma testaceum (Fabricius)	1958a
Apion urticarium (Herbst)	1978
Otiorhynchus clavipes (Bonsdorff)	1958a
O. sulcatus (Fabricius)	1915
Barypeithes araneiformis (Schrank)	1915
Cionus scrophulariae (Linn.)	1957
Orthochaetes setiger (Beck)	1915
Cidnorhinus quadrimaculatus (Linn.)	1957

ARACHNIDA

Opiliones

Nemastoma lugubre (Muller)	1954a

Araneae

Atypus affinis Eichwald	1972
Amaurobius ferox (Walckenaer)	1972
Oonops pulcher Templeton	1972
O. domesticus de Dalmas	1972
Dysdera erythrina (Walckenaer)	1939
D. crocata C. L. Koch	1972
Harpactea hombergi (Scopoli)	1954a
Segestria senoculata (Linn.)	1939
S. bavarica C. L. Koch	1972
Drassodes lapidosus (Walckenaer)	1939
Zelotes latreillei (Simon)	1972
Clubiona stagnatilis (Kulczynski)	1972
C. terrestris Westring	1972
Phrulolithus festivus (C. L. Koch)	1939
Xysticus cristatus (Clerck)	1939
X. kochi Thorell	1954a
Oxyptila blackwalli Simon	1972
Philodromus aureolus (Clerck)	1972
Salticus scenicus (Clerck)	1939
Heliophanus cupreus (Walckenaer)	1939
Neon reticulatus (Blackwall)	1939
Euophrys frontalis (Walckenaer)	1939
Pardosa palustris (Linn.)	1939
Trochosa ruricola (DeGeer)	1972
T. terricola Thorell	1972
Agelena labyrinthica (Clerck)	1954a

Textrix denticulata (Olivier)	1972
Tegenaria domestica (Clerck)	1939
Episinus truncatus Latreille	1939
Steatoda bipunctata (Linn.)	1972
Theridion varians Hahn	1972
Enoplognatha ovata (Clerck)	1972
Nesticus cellulanus (Clerck)	1972
Tetragnatha extensa (Linn)	1972
Meta segmentata (Clerck)	1972
M. menardi (Latreille)	1939
Araneus diadematus Clerck	1972
A. cornutus Clerck	1954a
A. cucurbitinus Clerck	1972
Zygiella x-notata (Clerck)	1972
Z. atrica (C. L. Koch)	1972
Gonatium rubens (Blackwall)	1972
Stemonyphantes lineatus (Linn)	1939
Lepthyphantes tenuis (Blackwall)	1972
L. mengei Kulczynski	1972
L. flavipes (Blackwall)	1939
Linyphia triangularis (Clerck)	1972

Acarina

Ixodes frontalis Panzer	1978
Anistys baccarum Linn	1939
Trombicula autumnalis Shaw	1939
Eugamasus sp. (Unidentified)	1939
Eriophyes macrorhynchus aceribus Nalepa	1978

MOLLUSCA

Marine

Lepidochitona cinereus (Linn.)	1939
Patella vulgata Linn.	1939
P. aspera Roding	1939
Littorina littorea (Linn.)	1939
L. saxatilis (Olivi)	1939

L. neritoides (Linn.)	1958b
L. littoralis (Linn.)	1939
Buccinum undatum Linn.	1939

Terrestrial

Pomatias elegans (Muller)	1902
Carychium tridentatum (Risso)	1969
Cochlicopa lubrica (Muller)	1915
C. lubricella (Porro)	1969
Pyramidula rupestris (Draparnaud)	1902
Vertigo pygmaea (Draparnaud)	1902
Pupilla muscorum (Linn.)	1902
Lauria cylindracea (da Costa)	1902
Abida secale (Draparnaud)	1884
Acanthinula aculeata (Muller)	1969
Vallonia costata (Muller)	1939
V. pulchella (Muller)	1902
V. excentrica Sterki	1969
Ena obscura (Muller)	1884
Marpessa laminata (Montagu)	1902
Clausilia bidentata (Strom)	1915
Cecilioides acicula (Muller)	1915
Helicigona lapicida (Linn.)	1915
Helix nemoralis Linn.	1884
H. aspersa Muller	1902
Hygromia striolata (C Pfeiffer)	1902
H. hispida (Linn.)	1915
Helicella caperata (Montagu)	1902
H. virgata (da Costa)	1902
H. itala (Linn.)	1884
Discus rotundatus (Muller)	1915
Arion hortensis Ferussac	1969
A. ater agg. (Linn.)	1969
Vitrea crystallina (Muller)	1915
V. contracta (Westerlund)	1969
Oxychilus cellarius (Muller)	1969
O. alliarius (Miller)	1939
Retinella pura (Alder)	1969
R. nitidula (Draparnaud)	1915
Milax budapestensis (Hazay)	1978
*Agriolimax agrestis (Linn.)	1915
A. reticulatus (Muller)	1969

Fossils and caves

Rodney Legg

FOR MOST offshore rocks, geology would be the primary subject, but on Steep Holm it is eclipsed by the surface vegetation and relegated into the most neglected of the island studies. Even the 250-foot cliffs that ring the island are often ignored as they are not properly visible from anywhere on the island, except the lower scree-slopes at Split Rock and along parts of the northern cliffs. A circuit of the island by boat can be rewarding but unless there is oblique lighting the relief and outcrops tend to look flattened like patterned wallpaper, with nothing of the dramatic qualities one has to overcome in climbing them.

The island's geology has apparent uniformity. It is composed of Lower Carboniferous Limestones some 330 million years old, in vertical layers, and belongs to the same formations as the Mendip Hills and Brean Down. While the island lies five miles from Weston-super-Mare and the same distance from the nearest point in Wales, it is only three-and-a-half miles from Brean Down. Much of the seabed between is only about 40 feet down, becoming particularly shallow at South Patches, a mile off the island. Though the island is essentially an extrusion of the Mendips, the strata on Brean Down slope at about 30 degrees to the north, whereas on the beach at Steep Holm the dip is in general about 30 degrees to the south. The Carboniferous limestone sequence is not entirely limestone—there is some sandstone also, and a coarse pebbly layer on the rock platform between the beach and South Landing.

The topography of Britain during the formation of Steep Holm is not well understood, but there must have been a large mass of land lying across North Wales and Central England northwards, while a tongue of sea reached up far beyond Bristol to the midlands. The present day sites of Cardiff and Bristol docks were, at times during the period, coral-fringed lagoons. At other times in deeper, bluer water the last relics of the Devonian period's great armoured fish swam slowly through great forests of sea-lilies and coral reefs over the place where Steep Holm would eventually stand in the murky, cold waters of today's Bristol Channel.

Until 10,000 BC, Steep Holm would have marked the southern edge of the north polar ice-cap. To the north, there was a continuous glaciation, and to the south the kind of conditions today prevalent on the south-east coast of Greenland and in Spitzbergen. So much water had become ice that the sea-level dropped considerably and the land between Steep Holm and Brean Down would have been exposed though permafrosted.

It is the position of Steep Holm that gives the island its principal geological significance, which was used by the Nature Conservancy as supporting evidence for the listing of the island as a place of special scientific interest. Prof. J. G. C. Anderson, head of the geology department at University College, Cardiff, has pointed out that the "relationship between the Carboniferous rocks of the north side of the Bristol Channel and those on the south side is still a matter of considerable doubt and controversy". The only visible links are the outcrops of Steep Holm, Flat Holm and Denny. Of these, Prof. Anderson says, "Steep Holm is the most significant" and he spoke out against any development which might cover or spoil the island's geological exposures, and added that future access "to study its geology is of considerable importance".

The island beds appear to belong entirely to the Syringothyris zone, which is visible on the mainland as the middle part of the great limestone exposures in the Avon Gorge. Syringothyris is quite a large shell, about three inches across, of rather pyramidal appearance, belonging to the Brachiopoda. Here, the use of its name

The island rock is made up of the fossils, 330 million years old, from warmer, coral waters. The tilted strata, seen here at South Landing, outcrop from the Mendip Hills.

Folded, inclined strata show strikingly on the island's east side. The only horizontal rocks are those placed by man, to build the inn.

relates only to the age of the particular layers. The Syringothyris Zone lies within stages of the Lower Carboniferous period known scientifically as the Tournaisian and Visean stages. On Steep Holm the strata are folded into an asymmetric anti-cline, with an axis running east-north-east to west-south-west "with the southern limb of this thrust over the northern". Part of this major fold is exposed dramatic-ally in the cove north-west of the inn. Fractures at its core, Rod Simm has shown, "indicate that the fold axial plane dips to the south at about 75 degrees." The rocks are mainly greyish-white and in part oolitic.

Limestone forms primarily from millions of microscopic shell fossils, but some-times larger fossils are found on Steep Holm, including several examples of a Paleosmilia (almost certainly *P. murchisoni*). These small carboniferous corals, about two inches across, are picked up on scree slopes. There are also goniatites and belemnites, badly eroded, showing in boulders on the beach. Brachiopods and Crinoids also show, the latter as stem-sections. Living organisms like these removed calcium carbonate from sea water. The limestone was laid down in sedimentary layers made up from the bodies of countless numbers of foraminifera (microscopic plants),

The southern cliffs are parallel to the axis of the island, and without extreme contortion for most of their length. The greyish carboniferous and oolitic limestones lack dramatic fossils, being formed from millions of microscopic shells.

certain seaweeds, corals, sea-lilies (crinoids), sea-mats (polyzoa), shells (brachiopods and lamellibranchs) and other small life forms which swarmed in the clearer parts of the sea. At the time of the slow depositing of the Steep Holm rock strata, this area was under the sea. The general character of the organisms making up the rock is remarkably consistent throughout the hundreds of feet of rock which make up the Carboniferous Limestone, although there are sufficient differences for the strata to be separated. It seems the rock was all laid down in roughly the same depth of water, although in theory the water should get shallower as the rock is deposited. This can be explained if one assumes a gradual sinking of a large area of western Europe at the same time as the sediment is gradually accumulating, and there are indications in other places that this is what happened. Not all limestone is laid down in this way. Some of Steep Holm's rock is oolitic limestone, which is formed by chemical deposition of successive coatings of calcite, generally around a tiny fragment of shell, a grain of sand or other material. Because of the appearance of the rock, which looks to the imaginative like fish-roe, it is called egg-stone (*oo-lite*).

While the negative side of geology is obvious all round the Steep Holm cliffs, with continuous if slow processes of coastal erosion crumbling the rocks, there is a positive aspect as well. Even in the present, land can be said to be accumulating on the island, though on such a minor scale that it is immeasurable. For during strong, dry winds from the south-east, fine sand is carried across the Bristol Channel from the great beaches and dunes of Bleadon and Brean. It is deposited visibly on the southern side of the island, showing as a thin rippled dust on the surface of sheltered paths. Only sand particles of less than 0.0039 inch diameter can be held in suspension by the wind, but these can be carried great distances. This, happening with a hundred times the quantities, is the clue to the surface geology of Brean Down, where large areas of the limestone promontory are covered by deep deposits of blown sand. Much of the vegetation has its roots entirely in this acid layer. Although this is unlikely to be a factor of any consequence on Steep Holm it is a reminder that coastal geology is not always as clear cut as it appears.

Geophysically, the island is 950 yards long on its west to east axis and 350 yards wide, with an egg shape, somewhat blunted at the east and pointed at the west end. At low tide, to the north and particularly on the south side, a rock platform is exposed, and at the eastern edge of the island a shingle bar stretches outwards. The size of the island expands to 1280 yards by about 430 yards. In terms of area, 50 acres lie above the high tide mark, and the island grows to 65 acres at low tide. The only part of the island that touches permanently deep water is on the north side of Rudder Rock.

Between the rock platforms and the plateau on the top of the island, at between 163 and 256 feet, there are steep slopes—inclined at 30 degrees to the horizontal to the south of the Barracks, but more extreme on the northern cliffs—broken by ledges of vertical rock. There is a curtain of sheer rock at the tide-line, all around the island, but this varies from being about 40 feet and climbable on the south side to more than 80 feet and formidable on the north face.

Jointing and folds in the strata show well in the slopes between the Split Rock outcrops and the sea-cut arch at Rudder Rock. There is also a dome-shaped line in the lower formations, visible at the beach, which conforms to the general profile of the east side of the island, with the rock outcrops dipping at a moderate angle to the south but vertically to the north. Other structural features include a line of mural and columnar tors and doorway-type structures midway down the northern cliffs near Summit Battery. There the sea appears to have reached this level at some stage. The mark of its presence is a wave-cut platform, now largely filled and turned into a slope by accumulating scree and earth, but still with some beach pebbles. Rising from it is a vertical cliff-face with eroded cavities of varying sizes. On the south-east corner of the island, between the sea-level Calf Rock and the base of the 200-foot Tower Rock outcrop, there is an area at high-tide marked by solution sculpture of the stone.

Towards the west of the island, especially at Split Rock and below Summit Battery but also elsewhere along the northern cliffs, some fissures are filled with

Opposite top: Another 330 yards of Steep Holm appear at extreme low tide, pointing towards Weston-super-Mare. This spit of small boulders is known to boatmen as "the cassey".
Opposite bottom: Looking back towards the island from the spit, the other low-water feature of Steep Holm is Calf Rock (far left). This is totally covered at high tide. The island's spit and rock platforms have an area of about 15 acres.

haematite (iron ore) and galena (lead ore). The lead is claimed to occur in quantities which, on the mainland, would have been commercially exploitable at various periods. Neither the Roman nor mediaeval lead industries of the Mendips seem to have regarded island extractions as worth the trouble.

The top of the island reaches its highest point near the northern perimeter path, tending to slope gradually towards the southern path, and although slightly dome-shaped it can be regarded as a plateau. A wide area around the Ordnance Survey's instrument pillar is almost level at 256 feet, and the path to the north of it runs consistently at about the 238 foot contour. Close to the Priory, the island's top has dropped to 215 feet, and at the opposite end of the island, between Summit Battery and Rudder Rock, the land is sloping downwards and passes below 200 feet. The southern perimeter path runs between 184 feet at the Victorian winch, and down to 163 feet between the Barracks and Split Rock.

This minimal degree of slope across the top of the island is insufficient to allow run-off rainfall to cause soil-loss, and the limestone tends to act like a sponge. Soil accumulates, rather than being lost, and wind erosion does not seem to be a problem even on the exposed top of the island. In places the soil on the high plateau is between six inches and a foot in depth. It is thin and red, stained by the iron in the rock. Underneath, there appear to be extensive crushed stalactite formations. Digging carried out between the Ordnance Survey pillar and Tombstone Battery in 1975, by a caving group from Locking RAF station, uncovered extensive fragments.

The caves on the side of the island and at sea-level provide the most fascinating aspects of Steep Holm geology for the layman. They are at two levels, the majority open to the sea at the high-tide mark, and others at the one-time sea level midway up the northern cliffs. The latter batch are now dry and no longer growing. Those on the shore, however, are below the island's water table and very much alive. Spring-water seeping from phreatic passages causes calcareous deposits and stalactites, though stalagmites cannot grow as the floor is too often washed out by the sea. Cross-rifts and other enlargements form where different solutions meet. Hall Cave, in the north corner of the second cove after the Inn, along the north-east side of the island, is a typical smoothly-rounded cavity, 40 feet deep, 20 feet wide and 18 feet high. At the far end it has a small phreatic bell—a hemispherical intrusion into the rear wall. The entrance to Hall Cave is through a knee-deep tide pool ten feet across, closely overhung by an arch of rock, and not to be crossed in swimming trunks as it may conceal a conger eel.

The other danger in entering Hall Cave is being cut off by the rising tide which rapidly fills the cove outside. To add to the sense of impending doom, anyone foolish enough to disregard the tides or the state of the water—in a north-easterly gale the sea can pile waves into this cave even at low-tide—there is an accompanying eery 'music'. Colin Rogers, a Mendip caver, reports that the chamber is notable for its echoes: "A nearby blow-hole in the cliffs outside can also produce an awesome booming sound in the chamber at certain states of the tide."

Only a few feet to the south, in Jubilee Cave, there is a more advanced chamber. It is similar to Hall Cave in size, but higher as rocks have broken away from the roof and cracks opened where the weak carbonic acid, atmospheric carbon dioxide dissolved in rainwater, drips through the porous rock. Below these joints and cracks

Top: *Calf Rock appearing as a pinnacle, photographed from the South Landing. At normal high tide Calf Rock is completely submerged. The extreme tidal range of the Bristol Channel is usually taken for granted, but the continual emergence and disappearance of Calf Rock makes the point rather well.*

Bottom: *Facing Calf Rock, the landward side of Steep Holm is sheer sharp cliff. The summit is 200 feet above. Its lower rock is pitted with solution sculpture, eroded by seawater.*

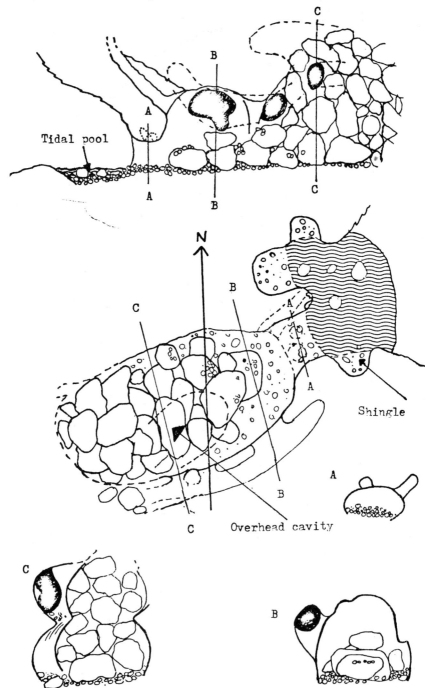

Tidal pool

N

C

B

A

Shingle

A

B

Overhead cavity

C

C

B

196

there are piles of rubble. Obscure passages lead into a variety of cave formations. Here Rogers found a pile of old bat droppings in February 1975. The cave has deposits of red ochre, stalactite straws and flowstone, on which there is some microflora.

The greatest interest in Hall and Jubilee caves is not inside but outside, as Rogers reports: "Features around the bay immediately in front of these two caves and their tide pools indicate they once belonged to one, much larger cave. A magnificent arching promontory of rock, opposite Hall Cave, appears to have been the backwall of a chamber. Many phreatic pockets around the area support this impression. The two existing caves are only back-chambers of the main cave. The floor of the bay is criss-crossed with haematite and galena veins. To the west there are several blow-holes that throw water-spouts when the sea is rough."

Neither cave, however, equates with F.A.Knight's turn-of-the-century description

Above: The sea has broken through into an ancient cave at the north-east corner of the island. This was probably its floor, but now only the back cavities survive. The larger of them, Hall Cave, extends 40 feet into the island.
Opposite: Jubilee Cave, drawn by Colin Rogers, showing plan (centre), elevation (top) and three sections (bottom).

The north-east side of the island, showing the water-bearing rocks, their moisture coming not from the island but the hydrostatic pressure of the Mendip Hills. Hall and Jubilee caves are below tide-line, left of centre, but Five Johns Cave (right of centre, in the area of dark shadow) is well above sea level and remains unexplored.

of a massive chamber named Church Cave: "On the north side of Steep Holm there is a cave running deep into the island. It is difficult of access and although above high-water, can only be reached at low tide. It was visited about 1880 by two men from Weston, who brought away a number of stalactites of great size and beauty. They also saw bats in great masses hanging on the roof. The explorers crawled through a narrow passage into a much more spacious chamber beyond. From the roof of this hung many fine stalactites, and the floor was covered with a sheet of water."

Of the other known caves along the northern shore, none answers this description. Five Johns Cave is a massive resurgence, possibly the back-wall of another large cave washed out by the sea, about fifty yards west of Hall Cave and some 35 feet above low-water. Tree Cave, a large dry opening halfway up the cliff, to the west of Tombstone Battery, is 25 feet high with an opening at the top and an elder tree growing from the floor of the cave behind its bottom arch. Steps Cave, further west and just above the northern searchlight post, is a small phreatic cavity in a haematite vein. It is less than ten feet deep and its main interest is an apparently undisturbed floor which may contain dateable material. Another cavity, above and level with the beach wall, called Hole Passage, is at least thirty feet deep but does not seem to lead to anything longer than a five-foot wide chamber. Raven's-nest Cave on the north face of Tower Rock is a smaller than average cave, no more than three-feet deep, and is a mid-cliff phreatic fissure, though now dry.

None of these caves in any way meets Knight's account. On the other hand if there is a single one-word error in his account it could be met perfectly, by substituting the word "south" for Knight's "north". This may not be pushing probability very far as Knight, like anyone knowing Steep Holm and its caves, would immediately think of the northern face of the island. The only one he is likely to have remembered on the southern shore, Reservoir Cavity, is no more than a dammed trickle. Water seepages otherwise seem restricted to the north-east corner of the island. However, between Reservoir Cavity and Split Rock, there is a hole in the rock-face called Window Cave. Behind it a bedding plane or fault runs from south-west (where it is open to the sea) to north-east, and continues for 70 feet, to a salt water rock-pool 30 feet long. Here is the only location at present known on Steep Holm where there is anything approaching access to its reputed hollow interior, and further investigation in Window Cave may at least show traces of destroyed stalactites.

All the evidence suggests that Steep Holm has an exceptionally stable water table far too reliable for an ordinary island catchment. It may well be supplied by hydrostatic pressure from the mainland, as was mentioned in the military chapter. This may be the clue to the growth of these cavities. Extreme rains, such as in October 1976 when the Mendips were saturated, caused water to overflow like a tap on the island, running from a crack in the rock-face near the telephone cable-house above the inn. This point is about 30 feet above the beach, at a similar level to the mediaeval well, and the water ran for a fortnight at the rate of 1,500 gallons a day. It continued for days after rain on the island had ceased.

Colin Rogers suggests that though the island's hydrological network is complex, an initial step in tracing its movements could be carried out by introducing a brightening agent (such as Leucophore) in the tank behind the Barracks and tracing any connecting passages. Strips of cloth could be tied in the mediaeval well; the resurgence beneath it; at a seepage near Window Cave; in Reservoir Cavity; and various trickles flowing below the tide-line between Reservoir Cavity and South Landing. Leucophore is coloured and typical of the brightening agents added to washing powders. Low concentrations show up on cloth under ultra-violet light.

Another research possibility put forward by Rogers, is to plot the variations of the rate of flow of the island's numerous resurgences with the rainfall of the Mendip Hills, Brecon Beacons and sea-level: "It would also involve collecting any true cave crustaceans from the island and comparing them with the Mendip and Welsh varieties. In this manner it might be possible to trace biologically the separations of the south-west limestone mass by the Bristol Channel, and the origins of local cave organisms, as well as an indication of the rate of evolution of subterranean organisms."

The study has progressed from an explorative to a scientific level. While investigations in 1933, 1935, 1956 and 1963 added some knowledge of the island's underground, it has now reached the stage where each new group re-finds the carbide writings of its predecessor. A nearly fatal accident in 1975, which left its victim hanging for hours at the end of a rope, forced the island's managing committee to curb the island's freedom to potholers. The Trust regretfully decided to forbid all future use of the island for general caving and rock climbing. This is owing to the obvious difficulties of bringing help in emergencies.

Opposite: The exposed limestone of Split Rock. Beneath this outcrop there is a cavity pounded by the sea. But it is between here and South Landing that Window Cave may eventually yield the legendary Church Cave which provided a Victorian boatload of stalactites.

Prospects of a dam

Rodney Legg

THE EXCEPTIONAL geography of semi-landlocked stretches of water facing the open sea, as with the Severn estuary, creates funnelling of the tides, and remarkable differences in level between the lowest of ebb tides and the highest spring flows. The difference is 14 to 15 metres in the Severn, and it is often said to have the greatest tide-range in the world, though Ungara Bay in Canada can manage more than 16 metres.

With these facts in mind, plus the marked psychological and practical turn towards consideration and investment in the ways of using natural energy—given the impetus of dwindling fossil fuels, and the dread of the plutonium alternative— it is regarded by many as likely that the Severn tide-flow will eventually be harnessed. The estuary has a three million population near its shores, and the concept of a hydrotidal scheme is attractive. Already, pilot experiments on a small scale at La Rance in Brittany have been successful and provided the necessary expertise and experience.

One of the most seriously considered plans proposed a 15-mile dam across the conveniently shallow waters of the Bristol Channel from Brean Down to the Welsh coast, incorporating both Steep Holm and Flat Holm on the way. Not that the idea is new to Britain. Ramsay MacDonald's cabinet approved a feasibility study into the possibilities of a Severn barrage on 9 July 1923. The study group was set up in 1925 and reported in 1933. This country was then closer to its age of great construction works. The Dutch are always credited with the ability to build dams with apparent ease, but a length of breakwater equal to that necessary to dam the Severn was built in England in the 19th century, across far deeper water, to make a four-square-mile harbour of refuge at Portland.

There is unlikely to be just a simple barrier across the Bristol Channel as that would too narrowly restrict the number of hours during which the scheme would be capable of producing power. As well as the main dam, a large holding reservoir— to capture some of the surging water and stagger its release—would also be necessary. That would need the deepest water available, and a possible best site is immediately

A mile offshore, between Steep Holm and Brean Down, there are only a couple of fathoms under South Patches at low tide. High tide, however, surges through to put another 15 metres under this buoy. That is the whole point about the Severn as an energy resource.

south of Steep Holm. This could be encircled by a great loop extending outwards from the west and east tips of the island and reaching towards Bridgwater Bay. The water would spin turbines to produce the power, at a construction cost estimated at between three and four thousand million pounds by a government report in 1977.

The prospects of Steep Holm being physically destroyed as a quarry for these dams was mentioned at a seminar packed with envoys from the nation's construction industry, held on 7 September 1977. Dr. Tom Shaw of Bristol University told Tony Benn, the Secretary of State for Energy: "It is easy and dangerous to draw lines on a map. The impression is given that the barrage needs to hang on to Steep Holm. I shudder when I see my name attached to something driving through Steep Holm."

Whatever scheme eventually wins, the most likely date for a go-ahead on the

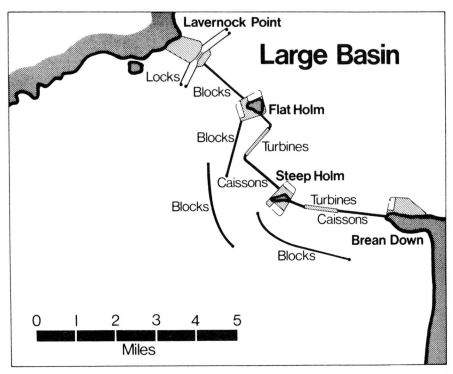

Above and right: Alternative barrage schemes considered by the Netherlands Engineering Consultants Foundation to be "technically feasible" in 1976.

project is in the 1990s, when the nation will be flush with the riches of North Sea oil and capable of pouring billions of pounds into its construction industry, which may be slack when the needs of the motorway and housing programmes have been met. Ecologically, the upper Bristol Channel is going to become a different kind of marine environment—one in which blue waters will return as the lessened tide-flow causes the sea to drop its sediment. Despite there seeming to be so much mud at the moment, a paper produced by the Institute of Geological Studies, entitled *The geology of the Severn barrage area*, shows—contrary to past assumptions—that much of the estuary between Brean Down and Lavernock Point has exposed bedrock on the seabed. Clear water would automatically increase the quantities of fish and marine plant-life. That in turn (given also the added advantages resulting from calmer water) must greatly increase its holding capacity for seabirds and waterfowl. Unless, that is, with the volume of pollutants the whole thing turns green like Lake Erie.

Blue or green, the present hazardous waters would become immediately attractive to masses of yachts and small boats, in the sort of density that plagues Poole Harbour. With this prospect of lasting ecological conflict, the birds are going to need Steep Holm even more than they do at the moment, and it can become the

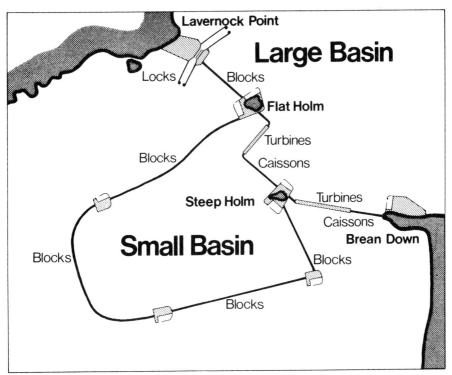

The "small basin" would have water pumped into it at night, for release during daytime peak power periods.

one practical symbol of stability in a transformed environment. Its greatest threat may come not from the dam builders themselves, who can be manipulated via public inquiries, letters in the *Times*, and deputations to Whitehall, but from the inevitable pressures brought by increase in leisure appeal.

Such changes could hardly be compatible with the present use of the Bristol Channel as an open sewer. Industrial pollutants from the northern shoreline, and Bristol itself, are the most obvious threats to the purity of the water, plus an emergency pipeline for radioactive waste from the Hinckley Point reactors, and a weekly tanker service from the Avon to discharge the conurbation's sewage. This vessel usually dumps its load downstream from Steep Holm, but on 20 May 1977 it emptied only a mile south-east of the island. The waters of the Bristol Channel are not generally deep. A trough half a mile north-west of Rudder Rock, at 19 fathoms is one of the deepest points in the Severn estuary. Further north, 5,000 feet south-west of Flat Holm, the seabed is only three fathoms, with a wreck known as the Mackenzie School. The greatest depth between Weston and Steep Holm is 12 fathoms, though there is only two fathoms of water under the South Patches buoy at low tide.

The work of Professor Heinz Kaminski of Bochum Observatory in West Germany

Above: Steep Holm is a speck on the horizon. Must it become a quarry for a £4 billion barrage? Ultimately the decision is a matter of public opinion—which means it's yours. Opposite: Rarely, the waters of the Bristol Channel become flat calm and even turn from brown to blue. If a dam is built, it could become the biggest boating lake in the country.

using infra-red photographs taken by United States NDAA environmental satellites, shows that the Bristol Channel is one of the five British estuaries where thermal radiation data suggests there is little water exchange with the deeper sea. Kaminski warns that shallow waters of this type remain stable throughout the year, and are at extreme risk from pollutants, because waste matter flowing down rivers and discharged from the shore is not dispersed into the open sea but remains in the inshore zone. The Bristol Channel, for its entire length east of Lundy, comes into that category and is included in Kaminski's diagrams of "the environmentally sick areas of Europe."

It is possible, of course, that the Severn dam will never progress beyond an engineer's dream, given the construction and cost problems. But even if it is one day built, it is not inappropriate that Steep Holm should be part of the battlefield. Kenneth Allsop spent many years striving to save threatened landscape by provoking public debate and intervention—often encountering as much resistance from naturalists and so-called guardians of the environment as he did from the developers, bureaucrats and vested interests. That Steep Holm should continue to need defenders makes it the one memorial that Kenneth Allsop would have wanted.

Steep Holm

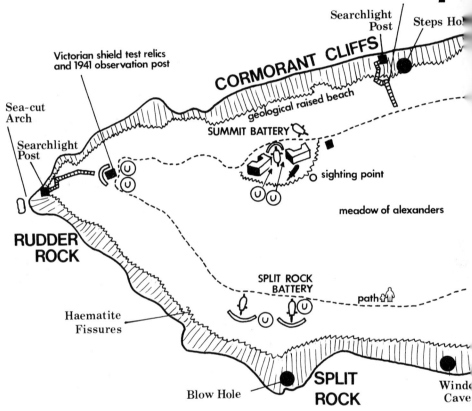

FLAT HO

208 Steps

Searchlight
Post

Steps Ho

CORMORANT CLIFFS

geological raised beach

Victorian shield test relics
and 1941 observation post

Sea-cut
Arch

Searchlight
Post

SUMMIT BATTERY

sighting point

meadow of alexanders

RUDDER
ROCK

Haematite
Fissures

SPLIT ROCK
BATTERY

path

Blow Hole

SPLIT
ROCK

Wind
Cave

Key to Symbols

⌒	1868 gun emplacement	⊙	well
←	George III cannon	ⓤ	underground shell store
⬧	Victorian 7in gun	✿	sycamore wood
☐	roofless buildings	●	cave
■	roofed buildings	⬚⬚⬚	steps
⌑	lavatories	-----	footpath
❀	peony	△	Ordnance Survey Triangulation Pillar

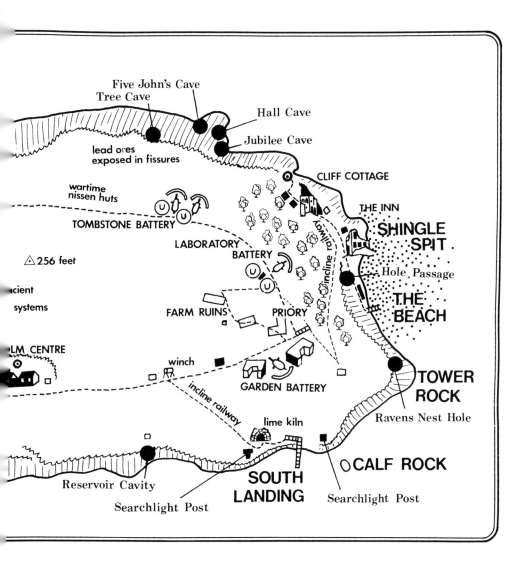

Map of Steep Holm

Malcolm Noyes

References

AS NO other book has been published about Steep Holm, further reading on the subject is restricted to various reports and pamphlets. In the case of some chapters, such as that dealing with the Second World War, all the research has been original. Though in other directions there may be background information in the material listed below, it should be used with caution as much is out of date. Most of the previous work is confined to the island's plant and bird life.

The first list printed below is of journals that contain frequent individual references to the island. Following it is a list of other sources, of varying degrees of relevance. Thirdly there is a bibliography of specific subject references and these contain most of the hard information.

SOCIETIES

Minutes of Kenneth Allsop Memorial Fund, later re-named Trust, 1974 onwards. Unpublished.
Proceedings of the Bristol Naturalists' Society, 1873 onwards.
Monthly Bulletins of the Bristol Ornithological Club, 1967 onwards.
Reports of the Mid Somerset Naturalists' Society, 1949–1966.
Proceedings of the Somerset Archaeological & Natural History Society, 1849 onwards.
Reports of the Ornithological Section of the Somerset Arch. & Nat. Hist. Society, 1911–1923 (duplicated typescripts), 1924–1973.
Reports of the Somerset Ornithological Society, 1974 onwards.
Reports of the Steep Holm Gull Research Station, 1963, 1965 and 1968.

GENERAL

Brody, G.S. (1856) *The Flora of Weston.* Weston-super-Mare.
Collinson, J. (1792) *History and Antiquities of the County of Somerset.* Bath.
Coysh, A.W., Mason, E.J. & Waite, V. (1954) *The Mendips.* London.
Department of Energy (1977) Tidal Power Barrages in the Severn Estuary. *Energy Policy Review,* 23. London: HMSO.
Knight, F.A. (1902) *Seaboard of Mendip.* London.
Lewis, S. (1955) *The Breeding Birds of Somerset and their Eggs.* Ilfracombe.
Murray, R.P. (1896) *The Flora of Somerset.* Taunton.
Page, W. (ed) (1906) *Victoria County History of Somerset.* vol. i. London.

Page, W. (ed) (1911) *Victoria County History of Somerset.* vol. ii. London.
Palmer, E.M. & Ballance, D.K. (1968) *The Birds of Somerset.* London.
Rutter, J. (1829) *Delineations of the North-Western Division of the County of Somerset.* London.
Shaw, T.L. (ed) (1977) *An environmental appraisal of the Severn Barrage.* 2nd. ed. Bristol.
Skinner, J. (1832) *The Skinner Journals.* Unpublished.
Smith, C. (1869) *The Birds of Somersetshire.* London.
Storrie, J. (1886) *Flora of Cardiff.* Cardiff Naturalists' Society.
Swanton, E.W. (1912) *The Mollusca of Somerset.* Som. Arch. & Nat. Hist. Soc.
Turner, A.H. (1955) *Lepidoptera of Somerset.* Som. Arch. & Nat. Hist. Soc.
Watson, W. (1930) *The Lichens of Somerset.* Som. Arch. & Nat. Hist. Soc.
White, J.W. (1912) *The Bristol Flora.* Bristol.
Wiglesworth, J. Personal journals and letters, 1911–1917. Unpublished.
Wilson, W.A. (1958) *Coleoptera of Somerset.* Som. Arch. & Nat. Hist. Soc.

SPECIFIC SUBJECTS

Allsop Memorial Trust. (1976) Deeds to the island. Unpublished.
Avon Planning Department. (1975) Report on Steep Holm. Unpublished.
Bantock, C.R. (1974) Cepaea nemoralis on Steep Holm. *Proc. malac. Soc.* London. **41.** 223.
Bates Harbin, E.A. (1916) The Priory of St. Michael on the Steep Holme. *Proc. Som. Arch. & Nat. Hist. Soc.* **62.** 26–45.
Beer, J.V. (1964) The Great Black-backed Gull. *Rep. S.H. Gull Res. Stn.* **1.** 25–26.
Beer, J.V. (1966) The Great Black-backed Gull. *Rep. S.H. Gull Res. Stn.* **2.** 18–19.
Beer, J.V. (1966) The pathology of the gulls on Steep Holm. *Rep. S.H. Gull Res. Stn.* **2.** 16–17.
Beer, J.V. (1969) Observations on the dispersal of gulls marked on Steep Holm and the Denny. *Rep. S.H. Gull Res. Stn.* **3.** 4–10.
Boyd, H. (1949) The Terrestrial Isopoda of Steep Holm. *Proc. Bristol Nat. Soc.* **27.** 483–485.
Bridgewater, P. (1968) The Vegetation of Steep Holm Island, Somerset. *Journ. Durham Univ. Biol. Soc.* **14.**
Bridgewater, P. (1969) A preliminary investigation into the plant communities of Steep Holm in August, 1966. *Rep. S.H. Gull Res. Stn.* **3.** 32–36.
Bridgewater, P. (1971) The vegetation of Steep Holm, Bristol Channel. *Proc. Bristol Nat. Soc.* **32.** 73–79.
Campbell, N.J.M. (1976) Notes on 6-inch naval guns. Unpublished.
Cardew, R.M. & Baker, E.G. (1912) Note on Plantago serraria. *Rep. Bot. Exc. Club.* **3.** 28.
Chadwick, P.J. (1962) Migration on Steep Holm, Somerset, 1961. *Bird Migration.* **2.** (2) 127–128.
Chadwick, P.J. (1963) Autumn migration, Steep Holm, 1962. *Proc. Bristol Nat. Soc.* **30.** 332–334.
Challenger, P.V. & S. (1956) List of plants collected on Steep Holm. *Rep. Mid. Som. Nat. Soc.* **6.** 32–38.
Chase, B.J. (1969) Spiders of Steep Holm, Somerset. *Bull. Brit. Arach. Soc.* **1.** (3) 33–34.
Chase, B.J. (1971) The Spider Fauna of Steep Holm. *Proc. Bristol Nat. Soc.* **32.** 70–72.
Chase, B.J. (1972) The Spider Fauna of Steep Holm: Addendum. *Proc. Bristol Nat. Soc.* **32.** 161–162.
Cowley, J. (1954) Records of Arachnida in Somerset. *Proc. Som. Arch. & Nat. Hist. Soc.* **98.** 153–156.
Crampton, D.M. (1964) The Blackbird on Steep Holm. *Rep. S.H. Gull Res. Stn.* **1.** 23–25.
Dilks, T.B. (1939) Thomas Clark's account of a visit to Steep Holm in 1831. *Proc. Bristol Nat. Soc.* ser. 4; 8. 460–463.
Druce, C.G. (1910) Plants of Steep Holme. *The Naturalist.* 227.
Ferns, P. (1975) Personal view on management. Unpublished.
Ferns, P. & Mudge, G. (1976) Breeding densities of Herring and Lesser Black-backed Gulls on Steep Holm. *Proc. Bristol Nat. Soc.* **35.** 85–97.
Garbett, H. (1879) Naval Gunnery. London.

Gillard, C. (1969) A report of Steep Holm slugs and snails. 1968. *Rep. S.H. Gull Res. Stn.* **3.** 24–27.

Gillham, M.E. (1964) The vegetation of local coastal gull colonies. *Trans. Cardiff Nat. Soc.* **91.** 23–33.

Graham, V. (1964) The Plants of Steep Holm. *Rep. S.H. Gull Res. Stn.* **1.** 2–9.

Graham, V. (1966) The Plants of Steep Holm. *Rep. S.H. Gull Res. Stn.* **2.** 3–5.

Griffiths, G.C. & Bartlett, C. (1915) The Natural History of Steep Holm: Entomology. *Proc. Bristol Nat. Soc.* **4.** 148–149.

Hamilton, J.E. (1939) A survey of Steep Holm, VI: Land invertebrates, excluding insects. *Proc. Bristol Nat. Soc.* ser. 4; **8.** 468–470.

Ingram, G.C.S. & Salmon, H.M. (1923) Great Black-backed Gull breeding in Somerset. *British Birds.* **17.** 41–42.

Legg, R. (1975) Thing about islands. Unpublished.

Lewis, S. (1936) Birds of the island of Steep Holm. *British Birds.* **30.** 219–223.

Lousley, J.E. (1954) Report on Steep Holm for Nature Conservancy. Unpublished.

Lovell, D. (1952) A memory of Steep Holm. *Avicultural Magazine* July–Aug 1952. 138–141.

Lovell, D. (1952) A naturalist on Steep Holm. *Country-side: Journal of the B.E.N.A.* new ser. **16.** 8 297–301.

Mason, E. (1954) Steep Holm and its Trust. *Handbook Soc. for Promotion of Nature Reserves.*

Matthews, L.H. (1939) Introduction to a survey of Steep Holm, and historical notes. *Proc. Bristol Nat. Soc.* ser. 4; **8.** 438–450.

McLean, R.C. & Hyde, H.A. (1924) The vegetation of Steep Holm. *Journal of Botany.* **62.** 167–175.

Murray, R.P. (1891) The flora of Steep Holmes. *Journal of Botany.* **29.** 269–270.

Nature Conservancy (1975) Report on Steep Holm. Unpublished.

Parnell, G.W. (1939) A survey of Steep Holm, VII: Entomology. *Proc. Bristol Nat. Soc.* ser. 4; **8.** 471–473.

Pearcey, F.G. (1915) The Natural History of Steep Holm: Invertebrates excluding insects. *Proc. Bristol Nat. Soc.* **4.** 146–148.

Pitman, R.A. (1969) Investigation of tidal flow from Steep Holm. *Rep. S.H. Gull Res. Stn.* **3.** 23.

Poulding, J.M. & R.H. (1966) Changes in the Robin population of Steep Holm. *Rep. of S.H. Gull Res. Stn.* **2.** 19–21.

Poulding, R.H. (1950) Bird observations on Steep Holm, 1949. *Proc. Bristol Nat. Soc.* **28.** 139–144.

Poulding, R.H. (1955) Some results of marking gulls on Steep Holm. *Proc. Bristol Nat. Soc.* **29.** 49–56.

Poulding, R.H. (1963) Infestation of Dunnocks with Trombicula autumnalis. *Rep. S.H. Gull Res. Stn.* **1.** 22–23.

Poulding, R.H. (1964) The status of the Dunnock on Steep Holm. *Proc. Bristol Nat. Soc.* **31.** 83–90.

Poulding, R.H. (1964) Fieldwork on the Dunnock. *Rep. S.H. Gull Res. Stn.* **1.** 18–23.

Poulding, R.H. (1966) The Dunnock population. *Rep. S.H. Gull Res. Stn.* **2.** 15–16.

Rendell, S.D. & J.N. (1977) Steep Holm: an investigation into the island's history. *Search: Journal of Banwell Soc. of Arch.* **13.** 22–36.

Riddlesdell, H.J. (1905) Lightfoot's visit to Wales in 1773. *Journal of Botany.* **43.** 290–307.

Rogers, C. (1975) Steep Holm Caves. Unpublished.

Roper, I.M. (1915) Botany of Steep Holm. *Proc. Bristol Nat. Soc.* **4.** 144–145.

Shaw, T.L. (1974) Tidal Energy from the Severn Estuary. *Nature.* **249.** 730–733.

Skene, M. (1939) A survey of Steep Holm, III: Botany. *Proc. Bristol Nat. Soc.* ser. 4; **8.** 452–459.

Smith, K.G.V. (1972) The Diptera of Steep Holm. *Proc. Bristol Nat. Soc.* **32.** 157–160.

Smith, S & Willan, G.D. (1937) The Geology of Steep Holm. *Geological Magazine.*

Smith, S. (1939) A survey of Steep Holm, II: Physiography and Geology. *Proc. Bristol Nat. Soc.* ser. 4; **8.** 451.

Somerset Records Office. Agreements and notes in the Kemeys Tynte MSS. Unpublished. DD/S/WH Box 48. Deeds of the John Freke Willes holdings. Unpublished. DD/PR/1 & DD/TH Box 6. Charters referring to the friary, from a catalogue of the muniments at Berkeley Castle. Unpublished. TB 2/36.

Stanley P.J. (1969) Report from 1965—8 on the Steep Holm rabbit project. *Rep. S.H. Gull Res. Stn.* **3**. 20—22.

Storrie, J. (1877) Notes on the flora of the Steep Holme. *Trans. Cardiff Nat. Soc.* **9**. 53—54.

Tetley, H. (1939) A survey of Steep Holm, V: Vertebrata. *Proc. Bristol Nat. Soc.* ser. 4; **8**. 464—467.

Tetley, H. (1940) Land mammals of the Bristol District: Steep Holm. *Proc. Bristol Nat. Soc.* ser. 4; **9**. 104.

Thomas, T.H. (1884) Excursion to the Steep Holm. *Trans. Cardiff Nat. Soc.* **15**. 88—93.

25th Field Battery. (1976) Exercise Sweet Holm. Unpublished.

Yonge, C.M. & Lloyd. A.J. (1939) A survey of Steep Holm, VIII: The Shore Fauna. *Proc. Bristol Nat. Soc.* ser. 4; **8**. 474—478.

Index